CW00408344

ANIESA BLORE

PARENTING
THE
CONUNDRUM
CHILD

The CAN do approach
to uncovering
their unique abilities

Re^ethink

First published in Great Britain in 2020
by Rethink Press (www.rethinkpress.com)

© Copyright Aniesa Blore

All rights reserved. No part of this publication may be reproduced, stored in or introduced into a retrieval system, or transmitted, in any form, or by any means (electronic, mechanical, photocopying, recording or otherwise) without the prior written permission of the publisher.

The right of Aniesa Blore to be identified as the author of this work has been asserted by her in accordance with the Copyright, Designs and Patents Act 1988.

This book is sold subject to the condition that it shall not, by way of trade or otherwise, be lent, resold, hired out, or otherwise circulated without the publisher's prior consent in any form of binding or cover other than that in which it is published and without a similar condition including this condition being imposed on the subsequent purchaser.

For all conundrum children – yes, you CAN

Contents

Foreword

How is it that Aniesa tapped into my heart when I thought I was reading a parenting book? As I devoured *Parenting the Conundrum Child*, I felt so many times that the story on the pages was taken from my life. My experience as a mom (or mum as those of you across the pond call us) of a conundrum child with 'additional needs', an Occupational Therapist (OT) impassioned by helping our youth gain independence, and wife (who also has been known to have a few gin and tonics). The raw honesty and the real-life experiences without any sugar-coating makes this the most refreshing and resourceful parenting book I have read. As the reader, I felt a connection to Aniesa, her family, and her heart, leaving me inspired to take a fresh approach to how I parent and practise as an OT.

Aniesa reached out to me a few years ago, keen to bring me over to London to share my life's work with her therapists and community. As an OT who had spent my career working with the pediatric population, I saw a heartbreaking need to teach the children with challenging behavior how to manage their feelings so they could participate in school, home and community life with more ease. I was convinced that the all too common approach by adults to 'teach them a lesson' by applying another punishment was not only ineffective, but detrimental to the wellbeing of these children. These kids didn't have the underlying skills to behave with more adaptive, prosocial behavior and no amount of punishment was going to change that. Many of those kids on my caseload were the 'conundrum kids' Aniesa describes in her book. Like her, I was impassioned to try to find ways to support these often-misunderstood children. I created *The Zones of Regulation* (2011) to help them be able to understand and better communicate their feelings, as well as find tools to help them regulate each of their four Zones. Fast forward a decade and I have landed in London with my family in tow to present on The Zones of Regulation and to finally get to meet our gracious host, Aniesa, in person.

Jet lagged, sleep deprived, and nowhere near freshened up, my family and I meet Aniesa after we drop our bags at our hotel. I recall worrying what she would think of me, of us. We were out of our element navigating the London streets trying to find this coffee shop and, mind you, my son has additional needs. I was on pins and needles waiting for him to meltdown; we all were exhausted, and what if he did so in front of Aniesa? I am thinking, 'Here I am, this "expert" she has flown across the ocean to speak to her audience on self-regulation and yet her own children can't keep it together?' I wish I had had access to her book first, for I now realize I had brought some extra baggage with me to London, my guilt, my grief, my worry. One minute with Aniesa and I realized I could let my guard down. It was clear she 'knew' me, the mom who is doing everything to keep the ship sailing smoothly while steering out of a tumultuous storm. She knew my son, who shied away from talking and gently tugged on my shirt sleeve asking when we could go. And I felt at ease, I knew there would not be any judgement.

Parenting the Conundrum Child assures me I am not alone on this journey, as well as offers a pathway forward for the parents, as well as the child. Aniesa maps out resources and tips to navigate getting our children support, while connecting with you through her journey and experiences as a therapist. It is as if she is there to hold your hand, which is something I know I have needed before. The practical advice is helpful for any parent, the case studies are relatable, and the message is clear (and received), there is no perfect parent, but together we CAN.

Leah Kuypers, MA Ed, OTR/L
Creator/author of *The Zones of Regulation*, Owner/President of Kuypers Consulting, Inc
www.zonesofregulation.com

Introduction

I realise now that my upbringing was somewhat unique – it has not only shaped who I am, it has given me an invaluable approach to my work. I was born and raised in a little town in Johannesburg, South Africa. I never thought about it as a township since our house had brick walls, glass windows and the classic asbestos roof. We even had metal security gates. Fancy.

I grew up in an era of Apartheid in a fairly strict Muslim family, and both my parents were classified as 'coloured'. I met my husband Zayn when I went to university – the first one in my family to go on to higher education. Zayn is white and didn't have a particularly diverse upbringing, so he had the shock of his life when he saw my childhood home. When I first visited his home, I realised why. The divide between whites and non-whites was, and still is, huge.

Despite opposition from his mum, we married half way through my final year at university. Zayn had to convert to Islam (the only way we could be married), so at least one of our mothers was happy.

When I took my kids to see the house I grew up in, they wouldn't get out of the car for a photo as they didn't feel safe. It dawned on me at that moment how different our lives and our upbringings were, just like those of the people I work with.

As an occupational therapist (OT) for over twenty years, I have worked with thousands of families from all backgrounds. I've helped a young woman dealing with sensory processing difficulties while trying to maintain a 'normal' life after years of trauma and childhood abuse. I have worked in areas so poor that I had to use papier mâché to make equipment such as walking aids, and in areas where owning multiple homes was the norm.

While doing the first year of a science degree, I applied to study both medicine and occupational therapy. They appealed to me because helping others, healing, making people better enticed me. I was accepted for both and my mother had to decide for me as I was out when the phone call came in. She told me she knew I wanted to be an OT, because I had been helping people to become more independent since I was young, and she chose correctly – although my main reasons would have been financial and the length of time I'd need to study before I could be independent.

I particularly love being a paediatric OT. Parents initially bring their kids to see me because they may have problems writing, playing, eating or sleeping due to sensory processing difficulties. Through occupational therapy sessions, the core skills we target improve: the kids are able to catch and throw (better); they can kick a ball without falling over; their handwriting no longer takes up the entire page and it's more legible. Suddenly, they are able to open their smoothie as their fine motor skills improve; they become more independent and successful. Many of them are referred on for further assessments and end up with a diagnosis.

Over the years, I have become aware of a cohort of kids being referred to me who do not have any diagnosis. They are struggling, at school or at home, with playing or writing, but their parents cannot get answers. All they want is for their children to be happy, to thrive, to succeed, simply not to have to struggle with what seems to come so easily to other kids their age. Parents want to connect with their kids, and feel peace of mind that their kids will be OK.

Trust me, when you have a child with additional needs, it's not about them getting into the top private school or playing rugby for the First XV; it's about them being able to get changed quickly enough after PE. It's about them being able to concentrate despite all the little classroom noises. It's about knowing your child can be independent in every way. But somewhere along the line, things start to go wrong. Subtle hints. Nothing glaring, but your instinct as a parent tells you something is off. They may sleep badly, struggle to socialise, not cope (or go) on playdates, find restaurants distressing.

Through my own chaotic parenting journey, accepting and coming to terms with my boys (between them) being labelled as lazy or 'not clever' before being diagnosed with Asperger syndrome, dyslexia, micropsia, sensory processing disorder, I have seen that once we as parents can connect with our kids, know and understand their goals, their abilities, and who they are, they can achieve more than anyone may have imagined possible. Personally, I stopped comparing myself (well, I tried) and my kids. I realised that success for my children comes from connecting, achieving, navigating through life, reaching whatever small amount of independence they can. And success for me means being kind. Giving back. Engaging. It means my children contributing to their community in whatever way they can. Achieving goals and being content, not just fleetingly happy.

Taking the learning from my personal experiences, I realised it could work for all parents of conundrum children. Once they truly connect with their kids, which means accepting them as they are, parents can fully appreciate them. Once the CEO of a FTSE100 company understood that his son would never go to Eton, but one day he would be able to live independently, the pressure was off. They enjoyed each other and formed a wonderful bond. Once a mum realised that her mental health was the most important thing for her family, and that working four mornings a week outside the family home meant greater happiness, she could be more engaged and focused with her kids.

Something big happened between these parents and their children – their connection improved. The parents understood their kids and their difficulties, and their journey together to success really began. The parents were happy, and the kids were too. And when everyone is relaxed rather than feeling stressed, they learn new skills more easily.

Achievement for the conundrum child is not about grades or a 'pen licence' or getting into a desired school; it is about independence. For Henry, it was about tying his rugby boots by himself and not having to run to his dad in the middle of a match. For Sara, it was about being able to read a bus timetable and use her City Mapper app without undue anxiety. When their independence increases, you and your child can navigate your way through your own wonderful journey to success.

I have written this book for parents who are seeking to be more connected to themselves and their partners and children. It's a guide to what to do when things aren't going smoothly, and you get labelled 'neurotic' or 'anxious'.

Regardless of what your conundrum child is struggling with, help or support for parents like you are lacking. Your child can't access the same services as a child who uses a wheelchair. They can't go to groups for kids with Down's syndrome. Sometimes they can't get a referral for help for up to eighteen months, depending on the postcode lottery. It's a puzzle, seemingly with no directions or support, no clear path or answer.

Parenting conundrum kids is super hard as they don't fit any one condition perfectly. Often, their difficulties are only really apparent once the child and their family have experienced considerable frustrations or social and emotional problems. The children are not born with a diagnosis.

There is no preparing yourself for having a non-neurotypical child. You get the seemingly perfect baby you planned for and dreamed of and imagine that love will be enough for the kids. While they're very young, you never imagine that the path your child will take will be different, or that your world will gradually shatter. This is because the conundrum child initially appears to be developing typically – reaching (or even exceeding) their milestones within the usual timeframe. In class or the playground, they blend in. Their differences aren't obvious, and it isn't until you spend some time with your child that you realise the incongruences in their skills or development.

As a first-time parent, you don't pick up on any anomalies until your child is around four years old. As a second-time parent, you realise a lot sooner that your kiddo is slightly different. It's not any one thing that causes them to puzzle you; it's more of a general concern about how hard certain situations are for them. When you mention it to your friends, you get the classic 'They're fiiiiiiiine'. But then your child begins to fall behind their peers.

As parents, we have all had the experience of watching our kids struggle in certain situations with things we thought they had mastered. If you have a conundrum child, this may happen more frequently, and be accompanied by tantrums or meltdowns. They may be less willing than other children to try even familiar activities when the circumstances are a tiny bit different. They need more support and understanding to be their best selves.

The parents of conundrum children have brought them to me for therapy, to develop motor skills or sensory processing. But they have all asked me more or less the same questions:

- What will happen next?

- Will s/he be OK?

- Who should we see next?

- Will s/he need a diagnosis?

- Will it help?

- What can I do?

- Is it my fault?

- How do I play with him?

- Will I ever engage with her?

Over the years, through my own experiences as a mother, and my experiences as an OT with other parents and their conundrum children, I have amassed a wealth of learnings that I now want to pass on to you in this book. Help is at hand; you're not alone. Part One will give you a guide as to when to seek help, the people to involve and how to work with schools. Parts Two, Three and Four will explore the CAN approach – connect, achieve and navigate – to provide you with some practical and proven strategies to allow for greater contentment through your journey with your conundrum child.

My hope is that through reading this book, you will realise you are enough as a parent, a carer, a partner and friend, and that your emotional and mental well-being must always come first. I want to give you the confidence to have a 'yes' day; to play to connect, and to connect to achieve.

Coupling my life experiences – growing up in a divided world, being married for over twenty-one years and parenting two amazing boys – with my unique insights into domestic violence, poverty, racism, autism, attention deficit hyperactivity disorder (ADHD), depression and anxiety, and helping families, I will show you how you and your conundrum child CAN connect, achieve and navigate your way on your journey. It's time to discover just how unique and amazing your 'inbetweener kids' are.

PART ONE
HELP IS AT HAND

1
When To Seek Help

In this chapter, you will:

- Learn to spot early signs that something is not quite right with your child and key developmental milestones

- Understand why transitions are important

- Contemplate naughty vs challenging behaviour

- Understand how to be a champion for your conundrum child

In 2008, I was doing some private paediatric occupational therapy work – learning on the job, as the saying goes. At the same time, Xavier, my son, started reception (his first year at primary school) and things were not going well, so I decided to set up my own private OT practice, Sensational Kids.

I remember friends asking how many clients I had, and me replying, 'Just one.' It was another one of my many crazy, impulsive decisions, but I needed to be there for Xavier, who had not settled into school at all. When I spoke to his teachers, they said, 'He'll grow out of it.' I went to the general practitioner (GP), who labelled me a neurotic Surrey mum (labelling parents as 'neurotic' or 'worry wells' is so disparaging and should be banned).

From the start, Xavier did not sleep. Well, he did, but only on the sofa at night while Zayn and I were in the room, lip reading what was happening on TV. This was the first of many signs we missed that our little man was not neurotypical. But in the leafy green suburbs of Kingston-Upon-Thames, all babies and toddlers were perfect, so we put it down to him being a bit different.

I was diagnosed with severe postnatal depression, hung my head in shame, took my pills, and berated myself for being a shite mum. Noticing more little signs that things weren't all they should be with Xavier, I kept putting it to the back of my mind. But soon the questions were mounting up:

- Did other children struggle to make friends too?

- Did other kids only cope with the same one or two babysitters?

- Was he the only child who was unable to self-soothe and go to sleep before 9pm?

- Did other children not enjoy their own birthday parties, finding them too noisy and overwhelming?

Then came the next big transition. We were so excited for our baby to go to big school. Little did we know that this change in Xavier's life would be more disruptive and eye-opening than we could ever have imagined.

He was in turmoil. He no longer saw his nursery friends. He had to go to breakfast club and a childminder. He had to wear an itchy uniform. He had to sit close to other kids on the carpet. He was so distressed, and we didn't know how to help him.

Xavier would come home most days and have the most spectacular meltdowns. And I took this to be entirely my fault for working and not being able to pick him up every day.

After much denial (more on that later), I gave in and had Xavier assessed by an educational psychologist. He diagnosed my son with mild dyslexia, and suggested Zayn and I get a referral to our local Child and Adolescent Mental Health Service (CAMHS). We saw a psychiatrist when Xavier was seven years old who diagnosed him with Asperger syndrome, along with tactile hypersensitivities and sleep difficulties. He then promptly discharged Xavier and sent us on our merry way.

This came as a massive blow to me. How could I have missed it? I worked with children, for God's sake. How could I not have realised? Didn't I love him enough? Was it because I was still on anti-depressants? Was it my fault? Was it because of my own tumultuous upbringing that I hadn't noticed anything was amiss? I was just so freaking proud that my kids were being raised where there were no alcoholics or drug addicts or domestic abuse that I'd overlooked my son's quirkiness.

Early signs

Something I hear so often from parents I work with is 'How could/did I not notice my child had special needs?' I hate that phrase, by the way – a conundrum child's needs are the same as yours and mine. S/he has *additional* needs.

When I speak to friends and other parents, they often ask what the signs were. What made me think Xavier was different? To be honest, I really didn't think he was that different.

We were such young parents, far away from family, working full-time. And not having been handed a users' manual when Xavier was born, we didn't know any different. Xavier was our first child. It wasn't until Noah came along – Noah who slept for hours and slept anywhere from an early age; who self-soothed; who didn't make a fuss when his nappy was changed (how embarrassed and ashamed I felt when Xavier screamed whenever I changed him, despite my best efforts to do it in a lovely environment). Noah who was easy-going and happily tagged along with other kids, didn't notice different carers at nursery, and certainly didn't react. This was when we realised Xavier was perhaps a smidge less than neurotypical.

I've spoken to many parents on the subject of early signs of a conundrum child. The one definitive sign everyone can agree on is that 'some things are just not right'. I know this isn't really a great help, but I guess when you know, you know. You may deny it or try to reason around it, but if you suspect something is not quite right with your child, then trust your gut instinct.

There is good care available when your baby is little. Your health visitor should be your first port of call. Not your friends – their instinct is always to reassure, and while this reassurance is well-intentioned, it can compound the problem. Not your mother-in-law, and certainly not the internet. Talk about your concerns with your health visitor during the routine check-ups.

All babies develop at their own pace in their own way. Some develop quickly, some slowly, some in stages. Some behaviours they display are part of normal childhood development, which is why it can be so difficult to spot genuine additional needs. Schools and nurseries don't test every single child for every single development trait, and so it is inevitable that some conundrum children are missed.

I cannot stress this enough – if you think there is something not quite right with your child, do not wait for teachers to flag up difficulties. Talk to your health visitor. Your holistic, intimate and unrivalled knowledge of your child means you are likely to be able to spot difficulties more accurately than anyone else.

Developmental health warning signs

Here are some signs that the parents I work with and I think are more notable or prevalent in the conundrum child.

At one year, they may:

- Refuse to cuddle or show affection for the person who cares for them
- Not seem to enjoy being around people
- Refuse to be away from their parents
- Be really difficult to entertain or amuse

- Show no interest in games of peekaboo – there's no laughter or squealing sounds typical of young children being entertained by this game

At two years, they may:

- Not seem to know the function of common household objects (hairbrush, telephone, fork)
- Not imitate actions or words
- Not follow simple instructions

At three to four years, they may:

- Be unable to ride a tricycle or scooter, despite trying
- Have difficulty drawing – they cannot copy a circle, vertical or horizontal line
- Show no interest in interactive games – they want to be in charge of the games
- Ignore children their own age, while being fantastic with babies, much older children and adults
- Not respond to people outside the family, or conversely, treat everyone as familiar
- Become upset when doing routine self-care tasks such as bathing or using the toilet

- Lash out without any self-control when they're angry or upset

At five years, they may:

- Exhibit extremely fearful / timid or aggressive behaviour

- Still cling to parents or cry when parents leave

- Be easily distracted and struggle to concentrate on any single activity for more than five minutes

- Show little interest in other children, and possibly refuse to respond to people in general

- Not express a wide range of emotions and seem unusually passive

- Have difficulties eating, sleeping or using the toilet

There is a myriad of developmental checklists available online, and some of them are very detailed. Visit www.theconundrumchild / parents-questionnaires. com for more information.

Transitions

Many conundrum children will experience significant struggles with key transition points in their life. They find it difficult to cope with changes such as:

- Toilet training

- Starting nursery

- Starting school

- Changing class or school

- Having a different babysitter

- Childcare – breakfast club or a childminder

- Moving home

- Going on holiday

- Christmas activities (this time of year is more distressing for some kids than we may imagine)

- Welcoming a new baby into the house

- Being ill

- Eating at a restaurant

- Play dates

- Birthday parties – their own or other children's

- Surprises

- Family coming to stay

These may seem minor to us, but our conundrum kids often struggle with transitioning. They don't understand why their environment is different, why they need to behave differently and why different rules apply.

As parents, we may respond by being structured and rigid. We know our kids and want to make their lives easier, and we want to make our own lives easier, too, so we only go to familiar places. We give our kids all their meals at home and stay close to the home or only visit close family. We anticipate that our child will find something difficult and prepare them fully.

But we can't prepare for unexpected situations – a traffic jam; a route diversion; a sudden downpour; the car not starting – that will occur and cause agonising distress for the whole family. As parents, we feel robbed of the enjoyment of play dates with other parents, the thrill of going on holiday. This is not what we expected from family life.

CASE STUDY – CONRAD

When Xavier was just ten weeks old, I had to take him with me to South Africa as my mum was dying of breast cancer. While we were there, I took him to visit friends and spent a couple of nights with my dear friend, Joan. Joan had fallen pregnant in our last year at university and had had Conrad while we were finishing our degrees.

One night while I was getting myself ready for bed (Xavier had just had a night feed), the door to the bedroom opened and in came two-year-old Conrad pushing a toy vacuum cleaner around, laughing gleefully. Joan and her husband were so tired, they had fallen asleep on the sofa, and hadn't realised Conrad had woken up, climbed out of his cot and decided to clean the house. Poor Joan was absolutely mortified when she heard the commotion, apologising profusely.

Several years later, I received an email from Joan telling me that Conrad had been diagnosed with ADHD, been prescribed medication and was receiving occupational therapy. I reminded her of that evening when Conrad had appeared with his vacuum cleaner, looking like a meerkat on speed. We still laugh about this now – I have in fact mentioned it to Conrad, who is navigating his way through a degree in industrial psychology at university.

Naughty or challenging behaviours

Behaviour refers to how a child handles themselves. It is how they act, react and respond to everyday settings, surroundings, circumstances and situations.

I love 'naughty' kids. They are fun, mischievous, disobedient; they play pranks and like joking about (I've basically described myself). Naughty kids push the boundaries but know when to stop. When you say 'Enough!' they know you mean it.

Challenging is a term used to describe behaviour that interferes with a child's daily life. When a child exhibits challenging behaviour, they may:

- Refuse parents' or adults' requests
- Get frustrated quickly

- Have tantrums that last a long time
- Have tantrums frequently in one day
- Be difficult to discipline (eg they are aggressive or seem not to care)
- Not respond to typical behavioural strategies

I will discuss behaviour and strategies in more detail later on. For now, it's enough to say that all so-called 'challenging behaviours' are just a child's way of asking for help. They are trying to tell us that they are struggling with something, but they don't know how to express it, what it is they are struggling with or what they need help with. As the National Autistic Society's Early Bird course teaches, when children can't communicate with words, they use behaviour.

Now what?

Your gut tells you something is not quite right. You become a little neurotic and start reading hidden meanings into your child's every movement. You check the checklists and, if you're like me, catastrophise. You convince yourself that your child has 'special needs' and your life will never be the same again.

You are both right and wrong.

Your child *does not* have special needs; they have *additional needs*, more specific needs.

And your life will never be the same again. You will likely read everything you can find. Listen to every podcast. Search the internet. Question your friends and family. You will discover words you didn't know existed. You and your family will go on an absolutely terrifying, exhilarating, emotional, dividing, confusing journey, which will lead to answers (most of the time), success and happiness. You will find friends in the most unlikely people; you will find your tribe. Then you will truly understand your child and accept them for the amazing person they are.

But first comes fighting the good fight. Stand up for your child. You are their advocate. You are their voice. Other parents and friends may tell you that it's all in your mind, that you're imagining things and being a pushy parent. You must stand up to these false reassurances.

And this is when you must push harder. Push with all your might. Go see the health visitor and the GP. Take your checklists, collect the evidence. Ask for a referral to the NHS paediatrician. If your child is at school, ask for a meeting with their teacher or special educational needs coordinators (SENCo). You may feel like you are not being heard or listened to, but you must keep going.

When you eventually get referred to your local paediatric service, you will be given an idea of the waiting time. Sadly, this is once again dependent on the area you live in. Parents cite the twelve to eighteen months waiting time as a major factor in them paying privately to see professionals – twelve to eighteen months in a little one's life is just too long.

But there are some reasons why I would be tempted to wait (and have waited):

- Things are slowly getting better

- Your child's issues are not getting worse

- Your support network is great

- Your mental health is good

- You expect no major transitions in your child's life in the next several months

- You simply cannot afford the expense of several assessments

- You have physical time and energy to follow strategies and exercises (detailed later in the book) at home

Key reminders

- Keep a list of all your concerns with examples of instances when each one occurred.

- Prepare your child for any transitions.

- Think about why your child may be behaving in a certain way.

- Complete the checklist – get in touch with professionals if you're concerned.

- Push for the help you want.

Now you know when to seek help, where do you go to find it?

2
The Professionals

In this chapter, you will:

- Learn that you are one of the 'professionals'
- Learn what occupational therapy is
- Understand the process of a private assessment and how to read the report
- Learn about the different professionals you may encounter and their roles

One of the most daunting aspects of trying to unpick your child's strengths and difficulties is the amount of people you suddenly encounter. Zayn and I were personally sent from one professional to the next, often choosing to pay privately because we didn't think it was fair on our boys to have to wait or struggle. I admit, we often used credit cards to fund these assessments and treatments, because this was the only way we could afford to put our kids first.

You don't have to have a formal diagnosis to ask for help for your child. If you suspect your child has difficulty with how they learn, or you're just worried about them, speak to someone. Ask for advice. Whatever your thoughts, I cannot stress enough the importance of getting a professional expert opinion, sooner rather than later.

You as the expert

There will be so many people involved in your conundrum child's life, including:

- You – their immediate family
- The school – their teachers and SENCo
- OTs
- Speech and language therapists
- Physiotherapists
- Educational psychologists
- Paediatricians
- Music therapists

The expert who is often overlooked, underrated or undervalued is you, the parent. You know your child better than anyone. You may not always understand them or know the causes of their difficulties, but you have such a wonderful insight into your child, and this is an incredibly valuable contribution towards planning their care and education. Yes, we as parents all need to increase our knowledge and skills, but don't overlook or underrate your know-how and instincts.

I always ask parents what they want to gain out of coming for an assessment. Sometimes they honestly don't know. They have been referred by their child's school, or they've spoken to a friend who I've helped, or they simply say, 'To understand my child better.'

One question I always ask the children is 'Tell me, do you know why you have come to see me today?' Their answers give me a fascinating insight into the parent-child relationship, as well as into how the child perceives themselves. It's important to speak to your child about their difficulties and ask them what they would like to get better at or change. I then explain what I as an OT can help with. It is also important to celebrate children's strengths, because every child has strengths.

After an assessment, I give parents and their child a brief summary of what I can help with. I don't believe in talking about children in front of them – I always include the child in this discussion.

If I have any doubt about a diagnosis, I share it. There is absolutely no point in being anything other than honest and transparent. And because I work holistically with other therapists, I will then refer the family on. But I always highlight that any diagnosis is just an explanation, a term. With or without the diagnosis, the plan of intervention and the process remain the same to work towards the child being happy, independent and able to learn and work to their full potential. A diagnosis does not define your child, but sometimes, it leads to access to more support.

What is occupational therapy?

Paediatric OTs always use fun, engaging and motivating techniques and activities which provide the child with sensory and motor experiences essential to developing foundation skills and achieving success. The primary goal is to help children develop, improve, restore and maintain those fundamental skills – emotional, motor, sensory, learning and behavioural – they need to form the meaningful interactions and relationships necessary for successful independent living and contributing to their community.

A child's main occupation is to play. Sadly, we expect them to do way more than that at a young age, and play is often scheduled and used as a reward or taken away as a punishment.

We expect them to sit still and quietly in a busy, noisy restaurant, where there are so many new sounds and sights, and then eat something that's not necessarily familiar to them. At home, they eat in a quiet environment with no battles (who am I kidding? There are often mealtime squabbles), and usually they are done in thirty minutes. Yet as parents, we get angry and irritated with our kids if they get restless in a restaurant when they have to sit and participate in an unfamiliar activity, sometimes for hours.

We rarely teach kids about their emotions or how to behave socially, yet we expect them to know how to do it. There's far too much emphasis on teaching them to write and count, when we actually need to be placing the emphasis on their social and emotional well-being. We expect kids to do all sorts of sports, yet don't recognise the importance of the time they spend outdoors, barefoot, simply playing. This is such a good way for them to grow and develop strength and coordination.

I hear so many parents say their kids struggle with cleaning their teeth, yet they never give the kids a chance to do it themselves, because they are rushing them off to school. Allow your kids to be independent in their self-care and daily routines – I don't just mean getting their clothes into the laundry basket, but actually learning to use a washing machine. Let them manage their bank account. Let them read a map and figure out which train or bus to get to school or their friend's house. We as parents need to stop packing our kids' bags for them and teach them to do it for themselves and by themselves. When they go to work, their employer won't accept 'My mum forgot to pack it for me' as an excuse.

The aim of occupational therapy is really just to make everyday activities easier for kids who struggle or find some aspects of their lives tricky, improving the functional skills that they require across environments. Making life easier for kids means giving strategies and techniques to teachers, families and carers, too. While the actual 'therapy' may occur within the clinic setting, OTs work closely with parents, teachers and other caregivers to help implement strategies to develop motor, attention/concentration, self-care and play skills in the home, childcare, nursery and school environments.

The assessment process

The actual assessment of the conundrum child may vary from practice to practice. When you go for an assessment at your local NHS/community OT clinic, it will vary greatly from borough to borough, and within different councils, but it will always be different to a private assessment.

At Sensational Kids, we collect information from parents and schools before the child arrives. This gives us an idea of how the child is presenting in different environments, and how similar parent and school goals are.

After our structured assessment, where we use both standardised assessments and clinical observations, we give parents some initial feedback, and then write our report. We discuss the report with the parents and make a plan which will suit both the child's needs and the parents' budget.

The report

Generally speaking, a report from a private practitioner will be much longer and more detailed than that of the local services. It can be daunting, so I always suggest that parents read it in two or three sittings. I try to write reports so that they are easy to understand, but it can be emotional seeing your child allocated scores which seem low.

Read every part of the report, and if there is *anything* you disagree with, you *must* go back to the therapist and query it. Do not just read the summary and conclusion and agree that the report can be finalised.

MY EXPERIENCE

When Xavier was seen by an educational psychologist, I did just that. I read the summary and the conclusion, and then started making a plan of action.

Zayn and I sent this report to the private school where the boys had had their first taster days. The school offered a place to Noah, but the head teacher said even though Xavier had fitted in really well and had a great day, his needs, as detailed in the educational psychologist's report, were too significant to accommodate.

We were shocked.

We then went through the report and found an error – it stated that Xavier would lash out and hit his peers and break furniture at school. This was not the case at all, but we had missed it. It was essentially too late to have the report corrected, so when we sent Xavier to another school for a taster day, we explained the error to the staff. Fortunately, they offered him a place. Phew!

Not all schools or local authorities will accept private reports, especially when a child needs more intervention and support than they can provide. I always tell parents to find out what precedent has been set in their borough, what is worth getting done privately and what simply isn't.

Making sense of the report

There are a lot of terms and words used in reports which can be confusing. I like using a bell curve to explain scores to kids, but don't let any scores or curves make you forget how awesome your child is. When I have used bell curves to explain scores and findings, it tends to be because the parents are finding it just as hard as the child to understand everything, and to help the child get rid of the idea that they are 'bad' or 'rubbish'.

To explain what a bell curve is, I use Buster, my dog, as my first example:

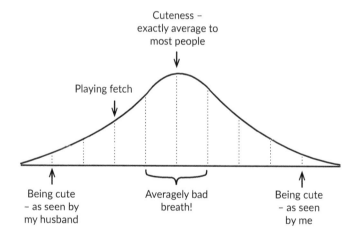

- He is dead average for being cute compared to most other dogs. Buster is amazing and cute to me, but he's no good at being cute to my husband (who's a cat person).

- He isn't good at playing fetch – he'll go get what you throw, but he often doesn't bring it back.

- He has average dog breath – an example where being average is not so good.

Now, let's take Leroy's bell curve. I *always* start by telling a child what they're good at according to the tests, what I personally think they're good at and what I enjoyed most about our session together.

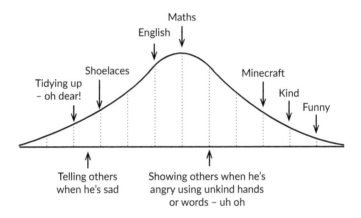

Our conversation may go like this:

- Leroy, you are way funnier and kinder than other boys I have seen this week. I enjoyed working with you. Thank you for trying your best.

- Mum and Dad agree that they think you are kind and funny.

- You and your friends think you are good at Minecraft.

- Your teachers think you are exactly average in maths, but you struggle a tiny bit with literacy and comprehension.

- Your lower score on fine motor skills (remember when we did the cutting and colouring in and pasting, and it was a bit hard for you?) means things like tying your laces are really tricky for you.

- Your organisation and attention skills mean you often don't tidy up – at home or at school.

- Mum, Dad and your teachers think you find it quite hard to tell them when you feel sad, and they wish they could help.

- Your teachers think you are better than other kids in your class at using unkind words and hitting when you are angry. This is something I can help with.

- What else do you think you struggle with and what do you want to get better at?

And just like that, you have set some goals. Voila! Real child-centred goals.

Other therapies

Children and their families do not live in isolation. There is no one size fits all intervention or treatment, and occupational therapy is not the only therapy out there.

These are some of the professionals I often refer to while parents wait for a GP referral to be processed.

Speech and language therapists (SALTs)

SALTs work with children and young people in mainstream primary and secondary schools. They are trained to provide specialist support for children and young people with a range of needs affecting speech, spoken language and social communication.

These may include difficulties:

- Expressing thoughts, ideas and needs
- Understanding what others say, eg instructions given in the classroom
- Understanding social interaction and making friends
- Articulating sounds clearly

These therapists can offer a range of support which includes not only working with pupils directly, but also providing training and advice to assist parents, teachers and support staff to develop ways of helping children and young people to communicate more effectively and access the curriculum.

Generally speaking, there seems to be more access to and better provision of SALTs by the local authority than other therapists. I have been lucky to work with some amazing 'speechies', both via the local authority and as private practitioners.

CASE STUDY – PHOENIX'S JOINT SPEECH THERAPY AND OT SESSIONS

I worked with a shy, anxious eleven-year-old boy. He came to occupational therapy initially to work on developing his core strength, as well as fine motor skills related to dressing himself and writing, but he also had a specific language disorder. This mainly affected his expressive language skills, but also his receptive language.

He was seeing a SALT at home twice a week, but they were making little progress. His mum asked me to liaise with the SALT because Phoenix loved our OT sessions and would often be really verbal and clear when doing a range of the sensory activities. I suggested that the SALT join us for a session so that she could get an idea of some sensory strategies she could incorporate.

Phoenix made a list of what he wanted to do, and within no time, he was engaging and chatting away to the SALT while swinging and throwing beanbags into a target. The SALT used this regulated state and we started having joint sessions, twice a week.

It was amazing. Suddenly he was able to give her directions, express himself and engage.

Paediatricians

Just as OTs work differently and have different specialisms and interests, so can paediatricians, but the ones I work with all tend to be quite similar in their approach. They provide advice, assessment and, if needed, a diagnosis for children with a range of difficulties that may include developmental and behavioural, speech and language, or specific learning disorders, ADHD and social communication disorders (including Asperger syndrome and autism).

I often refer children to a paediatrician when I want them to confirm a diagnosis of developmental coordination disorder, or when I have found a child to have sensory processing difficulties and want a further opinion.

Find a paediatrician who will work with and advocate for you and your child to ensure that your child gets the support they need.

Educational psychology

Educational psychologists (EPs) have extensive training in all aspects of development that may affect how children learn. An EP's assessment will identify the underlying factors that may be holding your child back at school.

EP assessments are broad based and cover all the different factors that may be affecting your child. What should you expect as an outcome of the assessment?

- A clear explanation of your child's difficulties and the underlying issues which are causing them. This may or may not involve a diagnosis.

- Individualised recommendations for how your child's learning needs can be supported at school and at home.

- Advice on types of educational environments which will suit your child's learning profile.

- Possible referrals or signposting to other professionals or services.

An EP's report is often used to support access arrangements in examinations, such as GCSEs and A-levels and IB exams.

EPs are like gold dust within the school setting, but SENCos can always request support, and you as a parent can ask for this, too. It may not lead to an assessment and report that's as comprehensive as you'd get privately, but it often leads to strategies that help teachers to help your child. But the waiting lists are often long, and this is why so many parents opt for a private EP assessment (although even their waiting times could be a few weeks).

I often recommend a parent to go for an educational psychology assessment when I suspect their child could have a specific learning difficulty. When I think they may have a wider, more neurological difficulty, I refer the parent to a paediatrician.

Behavioural optometry

When I first started practising, I learned about behavioural optometrists.[1] Some OTs I had worked with highly recommended referring kids to behavioural optometrists when they'd picked up visual perceptual and ocular-motor problems, such as poor tracking and convergence, but I must admit that their specialism seemed quite 'fluffy' and 'magic-like' to me. It wasn't until I took both boys to see a behavioural optometrist that I fully grasped their value.

Behavioural optometrists look at more than just a child's visual acuity. They will assess how a child's eye tracking movements are developing and can provide treatment to improve reading fluency. They will also look at the child's visual perception/processing and whether they have the skills that they need to learn to read and write at the correct level to achieve their potential. They do this through vision therapy both at home and within their specialist setting, then often prescribe specialised lenses.

---

1   British Association of Behavioural Optometrists: www.babo.co.uk/vision-learning

MY EXPERIENCE

At his first Year 1 parents' evening, Noah's teacher told us that he couldn't read or write and only wanted to play outside. I told her that I thought he struggled to read because he couldn't always see properly and asked what she thought. She was adamant that he was absolutely fine and merely 'lazy'. Goodness, I went full-scale mamma-bear.

I took Noah to the optician (again), who said his vision was fine. But Noah continued to struggle, and his self-confidence plummeted when it came to academics.

Zayn and I decided to move the boys from their lovely state primary school to a small independent school, which we couldn't really afford, so they (mainly Noah) could get more individual attention. I can remember Xavier was beside himself.

'Thank you so much for moving me. I love hard work. And it's so quiet. And the teacher puts me on my own table, so I don't have to worry about Fergus touching my stuff and licking my ruler. It's wonderful.' (Yes, I did raise my eyebrows about Fergus and the licking.)

Noah, on the other hand, didn't understand why we'd moved them. He was five years old and he cried every day for the first half term. Every. Single. Day. He didn't care that he was struggling to read: he missed his friends; he missed the games; he missed his old school.

After a while, Noah settled, but continued to struggle. Homework was an absolute nightmare time in our house. Noah would run away, hide, throw his books and cry. We would lose our patience, shout at him and each other, and generally just hate the 'h' word.

A colleague asked why I hadn't referred Noah to a behavioural optometrist – I had been telling her how he would read with the book either far away from him, or practically touching his nose. I also told her about his difficulties riding a bike and how scared he was, shouting that the ground was moving. It sounded like a functional vision issue.

It turned out Noah had an eye condition called micropsia, which explained his issues. This is sometimes referred to as 'Alice in Wonderland' syndrome.

The first time Noah did his homework after receiving his prism glasses, my husband and I steeled ourselves for the weekly battle. Instead, Noah completed about six pages of his workbook independently before stopping to see how much was left. Only one page. Screams and cries were replaced by one proud little boy and two relieved parents.

Key reminders

- You know your child best.

- Occupational therapy is about helping your child to gain their independence.

- Always pay more attention to how your child is functioning rather than test scores.

- Take your time reading any professional's report and ask questions until you are completely satisfied.

- Discuss the report findings with your child, always celebrating their strengths first.

- Think how you can help your child be happy or happier.

3
Working With The School

In this chapter, you will:

- Learn what the role of a SENCo is

- Find a list of questions to ask a prospective school

- Get a brief overview of what happens when your child needs more support than the school can provide

- Get a brief overview of the education, health and care plan (EHCP) process

- Learn about occupational therapy in schools

Some of the most frequent questions I get asked include:

- Which school should I send my child to?

- Will they get more support in a private school?

- Will they even get a place at a private school?

- Is a state school better than a private school at getting access to support?

When my husband and I chose a school for Xavier, we briefly entertained sending him to a private school from reception. But he had to be pulled off me at his taster day at our local boys' prep-school (a little red flag), and even though the school offered him a place, we decided against it.

We chose the primary school closest to us. In our area, infant and primary schools are generally rated as good schools, so we didn't even consider asking any questions relating to additional needs. At this stage, we hadn't yet considered that Xavier would need any accommodations at school.

When discussing schools with families, I always say, 'There is no such thing as the perfect school.' Conundrum kids can and do thrive at both state and private schools. They have a way of finding their little tribe, their niche, and slotting in. They may not excel or achieve earth-shattering results, but they are happy. They go on to high school and find their place. Some schools allocate one-to-one support to conundrum kids (sometimes at an additional cost to their parents, if they attend an independent school), and with a slightly adapted curriculum or environment, they do well.

Xavier was happy – he was never one of the struggling kids who went to small groups for extra support. And he was never in the top five who were given extension work or were super confident. He did sometimes get forgotten as he moved higher up the school – in the nicest possible way (I still see his reception teacher at his old school when I go to consult there and have nothing but the utmost respect and fondness for her).

But for the occasional kid, the school they are in, be it private or state, is not right for them. They may get lost in a big class in a state school. And just as often, a child, who may already have a diagnosis or be in the process of getting one, will struggle at a small private school because they are too different, too quirky, too needy. Or they are not able to overcome all their sensory, physical and other difficulties to achieve a level of academic achievement while staying happy and confident.

Choosing the right school is not straightforward. It is highly unlikely that you will find a school which ticks every single box. You need to look at all aspects of a school and make some compromises. Ultimately, you want your child to be safe and happy in an environment where they can learn to be independent.

There is a huge amount of information out there for choosing childcare, too, but when it comes to our conundrum kids, things are that little bit more challenging. Go with your gut feeling – trust your amazing mum/dad radar, and if there is a slight niggle at the back of your mind, sort it out. Be upfront with any childcare provider about your child – diagnosis or not, let them know how your child learns, any sensory or motor difficulties, how they cope with separation. Their responses to what you tell them will be likely to sway you one way or another.

When they're choosing a school, I always advise parents to start off by looking at the school they originally had in mind. Ask to see the SENCo and get a feel for how willing and flexible they are to add extra support.

What is the role of a SENCo?

Every school, from the early years setting up to Year 13, must have a SENCo.

The SENCo takes day-to-day responsibility for ensuring that children have their additional needs met. They often have *a lot* of paperwork to complete and spend their time coordinating how to meet each child's needs. More often than not, conundrum kids go to school without having any sort of additional needs identified. And their parents haven't thought that they may have difficulties or there may be circumstances which will make starting school or learning not as straight-forward for their child as it is for others.

The SENCo may be available on open mornings or days, but they will have to speak to all the parents there, so make an appointment if you have specific questions. Don't be offended when SENCos and teachers don't respond to you immediately – they often have a full teaching timetable, so a delay in their reply is inevitable.

When you meet the SENCo, tell them about your child and their needs. If you feel comfortable doing so, share any reports you may have on your child.

Some questions to ask the SENCo:

- What is written in the school's special education needs (SEN) policy? The SENCo should be able to give you a copy.

- How does the school organise its additional needs provision? Are children withdrawn from class for extra lessons in small groups?

- How does the school use its support staff? Are there teaching assistants (TAs) or learning support assistants (LSAs) working in classrooms, supporting children's learning?

- What training do the staff receive? This might be individual or as a group.

- What experience do they have of working with children with difficulties similar to your child's?

- How are parents involved in monitoring and planning for children with additional needs?

- How does the SENCo communicate with parents and carers? Email? A home-school diary?

- Do they provide any information or training to parents? If not, do they have a list of training offered in the local area?

- Is training available to all parents or only those of kids who have an EHCP?

- Does the SENCo have access to local authority SALTs, OTs and EPs?

- Do they train all the TAs and LSAs in delivering speech and language or occupational therapy programmes, or only specific identified staff? How often do staff get training? What format does it take? Is it hands on, and is it generic or personalised to each individual child?

- Is there a space where the children, whether they have identified additional needs or not, can go when they need some downtime if they're feeling overwhelmed or anxious?

- What do parents of other children with additional educational needs say about the school and its provision?

- How many kids have EHCPs vs how many are simply on the SEN register?

A good school will:

- Screen all pupils when they first start the school for learning differences, or at the first sign that they are struggling

- Have other pupils in the school with additional needs supported by qualified specialist teachers or TAs

- Ensure that additional support is an integral part of the school, with excellent communication between therapists/specialist tutors and subject/ form teachers

- Carefully consider what a pupil will miss out on to receive extra help and ensure they do not miss something they enjoy or are good at

- Have a supportive head teacher and strong senior leadership team

- Have excellent knowledge of the SEN code of practice and make use of concessions for exams, such as providing a laptop or a scribe

- Have good pastoral care

Some of my favourite schools to work with have a genuine interest in creating a level playing field. They:

- Listen to parents and act on their concerns
- Use multi-sensory learning and teaching styles to ensure every child can learn
- Understand when a child's needs are not being met and find ways to do so
- Continually monitor, record and review the child's progress
- Work with parents/carers to agree suitable strategies for the child
- Have some specialist help on hand

When your child may need more support

On the whole, schools are brilliant at implementing the additional support your child may need. Usually, this is directly related to their literacy and numeracy skills or their behavioural and emotional needs.

Schools get a tiny budget which is supposed to cover every child's additional needs. In reality, some schools have a much higher number of pupils with additional needs, and often these are more significant than the staff were expecting.

If your child is struggling in school, you will (should) already know about this, through discussions with their teacher and SENCo. If your conundrum child is exhibiting no difficulties at school whatsoever, I would highly recommend that you make an appointment to speak to their teacher. List the difficulties they are having at home and see if it is impacting them at school. If you approach this collaboratively and from an angle of needing support, teachers are usually helpful.

I had the pleasure of working with a great teacher whose own son is a conundrum kid. Stephanie Caswell is an author and teacher based in the UK. She has had a variety of roles within schools, including deputy head teacher, inclusion leader and newly qualified teacher mentor. Here she expresses her professional point of view.

EXPERT VIEW – A TEACHER'S ADVICE

Teachers are in a privileged position. We work with such wonderfully diverse groups of children and it's our responsibility to give them the best learning opportunities that we can. Working with children who have more complex needs can sometimes seem straightforward; there's plenty of support from external agencies and professionals to guide us along the way.

Conundrum kids are different, though. If teachers aren't careful, these children blend into the background, never really getting the help they require or the support they deserve. It's imperative, then, that teachers step in and plan lessons carefully. Building strong relationships with the parents of conundrum kids is important, talking about their progress regularly and agreeing on strategies to try.

From my own experience as a parent of a conundrum kid, I know it's so important that, once support has been promised, it's actually provided. Nothing is more disappointing than receiving a support plan, and then finding out at a later date that none of it was implemented. If teachers make promises, they must deliver.

Consistent support makes all the difference. You might not see the results straight away, but over time, the transformations can be huge. Talk to your child's teacher; embrace the journey your child is on. Don't expect quick fixes or a sudden change. Keep that communication with the school open and your child is bound to make progress, even if it's only in small steps. Celebrate those achievements and remember that no child fits neatly into a box. All children have strengths and weaknesses, no matter how able they may seem to an outsider.

With the love and support of parents and teachers, conundrum kids can, and do, flourish.

Ask the staff how you can be part of the solution so as to avoid any conflict. Always keep the school informed about any assessments your child has done and ask if the teachers would like to see the reports. I have found most teachers are genuinely interested in finding out more about a pupil's learning styles and needs, and as far as possible and practical, they will try out suggestions and recommendations.

The EHCP

Sometimes the additional support the school has put in place is not enough, either in your view or the school's. This is when an EHCP comes into play. It outlines any SENs a child has and the provision a local authority (LA) must put in place to help them.

Why apply for an EHCP?

An EHCP gives your child priority for admission to a mainstream school over other applicants and allows them to go to schools which are out of your catchment area, or even in another borough. It can provide for additional funding from the LA to support their needs and will often lead a child to gain entry into a special school.

An EHCP is a legally binding document which protects the support your child needs. If it states that a child needs twenty hours of one-to-one support in the classroom, then the school must provide that. It covers a child or young person up to the age of twenty-five so can ensure support or a specialist placement at further education colleges, but it does not cover universities.

How do I get an EHCP?

The best-case scenario is if your child's school is supportive and knowledgeable about additional needs. The staff can then advise you and start off the process for you. You can also contact your local authority's SEN department and request an assessment for an EHCP (some have a form to complete on their website).

Be sure this is the route you want to go down, especially if your child's school is not overly supportive. It is more often than not a long, hard slog, and can be emotionally and mentally draining. There are many advocates who can help you, but always speak to the school first.

What should I expect in the EHCP process?

After you have made your application to the LA for an assessment, it must reply with a decision within six weeks. If your application is rejected, then move straight to an appeal. This is a paper exercise, and more than 90% of families who appeal win their case.

Local authorities have been known to give some corker reasons for refusing to assess a child, which do not stand up in the eyes of the law. The only criteria you have to meet for an EHCP assessment is (a) you suspect your child has additional needs and (b) you suspect your child needs extra support in school.

The local authority, upon agreeing to assess your child, goes on a fact-finding mission. It gets information from teachers, parents, therapists and doctors, if needed. You then get a draft EHCP which you have a limited time (fifteen days at the time of writing) to respond to with comments and changes.

What if I am not happy with the proposed EHCP?

You have to ensure that the EHCP makes clear provision for your child's needs. I have been in many tribunals where the panel has come down harshly on local authority therapists who write provisions such as 'X will benefit from some occupational therapy'. The panel wants provision to be clear, for example, 'X must have six thirty-minute sessions of individual occupational therapy per term and six group occupational therapy sessions per term'.

It is important the EHCP reflects the child's needs on their worst day. It can be upsetting for parents to read, but the professionals contributing to the EHCP know that if they are not clear and specific, it could mean that your child does not get the support they need.

The LA is obliged to consider any private reports you may have commissioned. If you and the local authority cannot agree on, for example, the delivery of a therapy, you may need to go to a tribunal for a decision. The SEN tribunal process is incredibly taxing. Finding a good parent advocate or SEN solicitor may seem a bit over the top, but honestly, if it reduces your stress and helps keep you sane, then go for it. Don't try to do it alone.

Occupational therapy in schools

I have been fortunate enough to work with some pretty awe-inspiring SENCos and teachers. Schools have recognised their lack of OT provision, and so will often ask us in to do training around specific topics.

The training OTs do most includes:

- What is occupational therapy?

- Developing motor skills.

- Carrying out an occupational therapy programme.

- What is sensory processing?

- How to implement a sensory diet.

OTs use either a bottom-up or top-down approach when assessing and treating children. When using a bottom-up approach, the OT will evaluate and assess the child's underlying foundation components of function and develop an intervention plan based on deficits or difficulties within these components. A top-down approach is when the OT evaluates a child's functional abilities in relation to their daily occupations (play, self-care, learning) and uses this as a basis to draw up an intervention plan. A newer model uses proximal and distal goals to address both types of goals, focusing on the distal with families.

There are several frames of reference in occupational therapy. Frames of reference are theories which OTs use when deciding what treatment approach to use. Experienced OTs will often use multiple frames of reference when deciding on clinical intervention and strategies.

Some of the most common frames of reference used in paediatrics include Biomechanical, Developmental, Neurodevelopmental, Rehabilitative, and Ayres Sensory Integration® (previously known as Sensory Integration). It is important to note here that a pure Ayres Sensory Integration® therapy approach is always led by a trained therapist in a specialised clinic space or using specialised equipment. It must be child-led, while the therapist ensures that opportunities and activities are at a 'just right' level to help improve the child's sensory integration. Ayres Sensory Integration® is too often confused with general sensory strategies, such as using a sensory diet, listening therapy or therapeutic brushing.

Occupational therapy is focused on developing and implementing skill improvement and strategies to aid this across all the environments that the child encounters. Without this focus, children can become good at demonstrating a skill in just one location with one person in the one way they have practised it. Occupational therapy is focused on children being able to develop, and then use these skills across all environments to be the most flexible and proficient learners they can be.

Key reminders

- Don't be afraid to ask questions when you meet with a SENCo.

- Schools and teachers are not the enemy. Talk to them, express your concerns and ask to be a part of the solution.

- Not all schools can afford to have occupational therapy – ask the school how you can support any groups that are running.

- An EHCP outlines any SENs a child has and the provision a local authority must put in place to help them.

- Occupational therapy is focused on developing and implementing skill improvement across all the environments the child may encounter.

PART TWO
CONNECT

4
Lose The Guilt

In this chapter, you will:

- Discover where my personal guilt stemmed from

- Learn why I had difficulties connecting when I was a child

- See how guilt can be triggered by the most innocent of remarks

- Learn why you need to get rid of the mummy/ daddy guilt

- Read some tips to help you let go of the guilt and be kind to yourself

It's time for us to start our journey through the first part of the CAN approach: connect. But what exactly is connection?

When I searched for the definition of the word 'connect' online (because where else would I search?), the *Cambridge English Dictionary* said, 'Connect – *verb* – (relationship): to feel close to someone or have a good relationship with them'.[2] The *Oxford Learner's Dictionary* defines 'connect' as 'form relationship [intransitive]: connect (with somebody) to form a good relationship with someone so that you like and understand each other'.[3] But before we can connect, there is something we must disconnect with – something most of us carry around to a greater or lesser extent. That burden is called guilt.

The start of my guilt

When I was growing up, my parents shared one room, and I shared a room with my sisters – sometimes all three of them, sometimes two of them, sometimes all of them and my grandmother, and sometimes just one of them. Of the four of us, I had the strongest connection with my mother. I lived to please her. To make her happy. To make her proud. I wanted her to feel that something good had come out of her marriage to my

2   Cambridge English Dictionary, www.dictionary.cambridge.org/dictionary/english/connect
3   Oxford Learner's Dictionary, www.oxfordlearnersdictionaries.com/definition/english/connect

father (my siblings and I had three dads between us, a fact we discovered only after my mum had passed away).

My mum was Muslim, like her parents and siblings. She'd had me with my father, Peter, who'd converted to Islam and become Ameer. My dad was an alcoholic and drug addict. He was often violent. There were many nights he didn't come home, yet I loved him fiercely. He was my dad. In my formative years, I knew nothing different.

At school, I soon realised that not many other kids instinctively knew to hide under the bed when their dad came home inebriated. Not many of them would find their dads asleep on the kitchen floor and have to help him to the sofa or bed and take his shoes off, cover him with a blanket and kiss him goodnight. But when my dad was sober and present, we connected in a way I can hardly describe.

He got me. He followed my rambling stories and didn't think it was odd that I jumped from one topic to the next, almost out of breath, trying to tell him everything he had missed over the days or weeks he had been drunk. And even when he was drunk and high and offering me as payment to his dealer (God bless that dealer for having some modicum of self-respect and settling for shoving and punching my dad, smiling at me with such pity in his eyes), I still loved him.

To this day, I sometimes feel guilty for loving him so much, because I was apparently the reason my mum took an agonisingly long time to kick him out and divorce him. She didn't want to upset me. When I finally explained at the age of fourteen that actually, it would be good to hand in homework on time and not be exhausted from listening to the shouting and breaking of stuff, and not live in fear that his new dealer would take him up on his payment offers, my mother was both sad and relieved.

Dad left when I was fifteen years old, our relationship broken. Shortly afterwards, he committed suicide. The guilt my mother felt was insurmountable. And I felt guilty, too, for not trying harder to connect with him and get him to love me more than drugs and alcohol. He didn't choose me over his addictions.

My own difficulties connecting

I was a funny, quirky child, sometimes (OK, maybe more often than not) inappropriate and impulsive, but well liked. For some reason, most likely our domestic situation, I developed a severe stutter and my siblings had a field day teasing me. I remember my mum having to work, and my middle sister taking me to one of the big state hospitals nearby for speech therapy.

Nevertheless, I was awarded a bursary to a private school (funded by lovely Europeans). Most of the pupils were black, with about 30% coloured (as we were classed) and a smattering of white pupils. Having been segregated from other colours of kids, I realised then, for the first time, that everyone was the same and that kids of all colours could be equally mean or nice. And I learned that racism has no boundaries – the other coloured kids in our town used to throw stones at those of us who went to school with the 'black' kids. Looking back on my schooldays, I now realise that I had a really difficult time fitting in.

Not long after my father committed suicide, when I was about to turn sixteen years old, I wrote my final high school exams. There really was no time to grieve – I had to study and be strong for my mother, especially as I would soon be 'abandoning her' (her words, not mine). I had been accepted to study at the University of Stellenbosch. Before this, I had never been on an aeroplane, or even lived away from home. This would be the first time I would truly connect with myself.

Parental guilt

MY EXPERIENCE

When I had my boys, I struggled to connect with them because I refused to take my anti-depressants. I refused to do this because I felt guilty. Surely, I shouldn't have to take happy pills. I believed that made me so weak.

I remember going to the occasional baby group when I took time off work and seeing mums with tiny babies, singing along, smiling and laughing, doting on their children. 'What on earth is this new kind of hell?' I asked myself. Babies screaming. Mothers comparing nipples and tutting at those who were bottle feeding. Questioning sleep routines and poop colour.

And bam! The guilt winded me.

'You should be here with your baby,' it whispered. 'You should know the colour of his 2pm poo. You should know which side his curls flop to.' But I didn't know; I could only go by the detailed account the nursery staff had written down in his little home diary. I did, however, know that my cherub did not sleep. Not at nursery. Not at home. Certainly not in his room or in his cot. So there, busybodies, I could answer that question.

I struggled to connect with my autistic son, who would come home from a seemingly perfect day at school and have the mother of all tantrums, kicking and screaming, trashing his room and everything in his path. He was so overwhelmed with having had to keep it together all day at school that me simply asking him to take his shoes off meant he lost control.

I am grateful every day for this period in our lives, because when teachers and therapists say, while rolling their eyes, 'This child is perfect at school, but the mum says s/he is awful at home', I can vouch for the child's mum.

I can say, 'That poor woman. She must be exhausted. She must be at her wits' end.' Because I was.

Parents don't make up stories about their kids being difficult at home. Trust me, we don't want teachers and the whole world to know that we are struggling to connect with our kids. That we can't get them to listen or behave in a certain way. That we are not perfect. Why would we make that up?

And trust me, our kids don't act like Jekyll and Hyde to make us look like idiots. They do it because they are trying so hard to conform, to fit in, to be like their classmates. And they know, no matter what they do or say, we, their parents, will always love them and accept them. So, it's OK to unleash with us because we have such a great connection. When they're being feral and wrecking the place, it is the only way they currently know to communicate just how hard their day was. How distressing it was for the little chap with sensory processing difficulties to hear the school bell several times in the day. For the young girl not to move at all when the teacher casually but strictly said, 'Sit still'.

You try it, right now. Literally sit still – hard, isn't it? Hard not to scratch that sudden itch. Is blinking allowed when the teacher says sit still? Gosh, I don't know. Best try not to do it.

Just like us, our kids can't always communicate to their best abilities. I'm sure we have all left confrontational conversations and, when the stress dissipated, said to ourselves, 'I should have said *this*!' Our kids are the same.

Guilt – get rid of it

The perfect parent does not exist – you are good enough. And a good enough parent is pretty friggin' awesome. But you have to start by taking care of you. And taking care of yourself must start with getting rid of any mummy / daddy guilt you may have.

Deciding to return to work is either straightforward or difficult for any parent. I had no choice – I had to work. Zayn and I had no other income, and Xavier was well looked after by my husband. I had nothing to feel guilty about.

When I found a new job that would sponsor our visa, I was happy because the company had a subsidised on-site nursery. This was amazing. I remember my first day, dropping my bundle of joy off at nursery for his induction before I started mine. I can still see my sweet, naive face, brimming with excitement, until, as I handed Xavier over, the nursery manager turned to me and made a seemingly innocuous remark:

'Don't worry. He'll be fine. Don't you feel guilty, now.'

And just like that, my world exploded.

Being completely and utterly naive, I hadn't felt guilty – why should I? I was paying a fortune for qualified staff to look after my precious first-born. Why worry? My mother had worked, and I remembered being left with the maid (not very politically correct). My sisters worked and left their babies in day care or with maids. One of my good friends fell pregnant while we were at university and I often babysat her son while she dashed to and from work. I didn't know anything different. This is what the women in my life did – they left their babies and went out to earn money.

Sitting in the staffroom chatting to the other parents, I soon discovered that guilt seemed to be pretty standard, especially for working mums. I had never thought about this, so then I felt guilty for *not* having felt guilty about leaving Xavier at nursery when he was only four months old. And so started my tango with good old self-inflicted guilt.

I remember telling myself that our life in the UK relied on my working visa, so I *had* to stay employed. I had no choice. And that was what I told my new colleagues, friends, siblings in South Africa, and every other busybody who questioned why I went to work when my baby was oh so little. How did I cope with the guilt of abandoning him?

Yes, people used those words. And I didn't clobber them; I smiled sweetly and naively. I was only twenty-five years old and had lived most of my life in

Johannesburg, so I thought this was simply what people did in leafy Surrey – not mind their own business.

Then came a revelation. At one of the few baby groups I managed to attend, I was talking about going to work and using the nursery supplied by the company. As I spoke, six or seven mums were smiling weirdly back at me.

'Oh God,' said one eventually, 'I wish I could go back to work. I miss my job. I feel guilty for not bringing any money in.'

'Oh yes,' said another, 'I feel guilty for getting annoyed when I change yet another shitty nappy while wishing I was on a train to London with my standing-only seat.' And then it hit me – these sweet, seemingly perfect Surrey mums felt guilty too. About staying at home!

What?

And so it appeared that *everyone* felt guilty. The dads, too, for not helping enough around the house. For going to work while their partners stayed home, raising the kids. For rushing home and not socialising with colleagues. As parents, we were all becoming experts at competing – including at how guilty we felt and about what.

I, like thousands of other women, *loved* going to work. I loved using my degree and making a difference in children's lives. I loved speaking to my colleagues. I loved going to the loo without an audience. I loved our bedtime routine (if you could call it that – the baby books certainly didn't. Oh look, more guilt). I loved bringing in a tiny bit of money – after more than half had been taken for nursery. I loved being an OT.

Guilt will not help you be a better parent or carer. It simply focuses all your energy on your perceived mistakes, taking away your time to celebrate joyful moments. Personally, feeling guilty made me more frustrated, angrier, more impatient and more detached from my boys. I continued this vicious cycle – believing I was doing the wrong thing, making mistakes, messing up, then feeling guilty – again and again. Every little thing became a massive point of blame.

When Xavier started school, I felt guilty for making him wear his uniform and not realising there was such a thing as seamless socks, which made his life infinitely better. I felt guilty for enjoying my work. I felt guilty for getting cross with him when he struggled with transitions. I felt guilty when he sat in a corner at his own birthday party because it was too noisy and smelly (I mean, who doesn't love a foam pit full of screaming children?). And that guilt continued well until Xavier and Noah were at prep-school (yes, I felt guilty that Xavier had to sit in a class with twenty-nine other children and struggle with the noises, so took out loans to send them both to a tiny private school).

Driving home one night, after picking my boys up from afterschool prep (of course, I felt guilty for working late), I was chatting to them about their day, and they asked about mine. I remember telling them about the kids I had seen that day, and how one little boy had bum-shuffled for the first time, and a mum had messaged me to say her daughter had finally allowed herself to be hugged. I told them that I felt bad for missing a coffee morning in their headmaster's office because of work. And Xavier said something that I will never forget.

'I love that you work. I love that you love your job so much. I want to marry someone who has a job they love as much.'

And then Noah piped up, 'Yes, me too. So my wife can work while I play games all day and look after our babies.'

I was stunned. Where had this come from?

It turned out, the topic of careers had come up in one of Xavier's lessons, and all the boys had to say what their parents did for work. Xavier had told everyone, 'Mum plays with children on swings all day, and teaches them to write, and helps them learn to do things for themselves.' Apparently, a lot of the other boys had said their dads went to work while their mums drank coffee and complained about cleaning the house!

And it hit me – I had never once asked my boys' opinion about my working outside the home. About their thoughts on me dashing away as soon as assembly was over to go to other children. About them having to go to breakfast club or stay for prep while I rushed home. They knew nothing different, like I had known nothing different when my mother and sisters and friends worked and left the care of their babies to someone else. And hang on – they actually liked me working?

'Yes,' they said. 'Our friends say they wish their mums worked and didn't just drink coffee and go to the gym and chat to their friends.' (Oh, how I wish… no, not really!)

Don't enable the guilt

Guilt is totally self-inflicted. I allowed myself to feel guilty, so take note:

- Any difference your child may be experiencing is nobody's fault.

- Work away from home or at home, or in the home – as long as *you* are happy.

- If your child is not happy in one setting, don't stick it out; find somewhere you and they will be happy.

- Resistance is *not* futile! You do not have to do five baby/toddler groups per week if it stresses you out. If you like the group but the parents stress you out, find another group. Create your own group. Don't go to a group. Just be happy.

- Mum/dad/carer guilt appears because we love our kids so much that we want to be perfect for them. But – brace yourself – the perfect parent *does not exist. You* are good enough – and that is exactly the type of parent your child needs.

Guilt is the thief of all things joyful. It sucks the happiness out of parenting, and the sooner we realise that it's pointless, the sooner we can embrace our foibles and let go of the damn guilt.

Try these exercises:

- Be kind to yourself. When you learn to be gentle with yourself and shush the voice inside you constantly criticising you, something wonderful happens. You can let go of the guilt and start focusing on solutions.

- Accepting your imperfections and forgiving yourself for your mistakes doesn't mean that you don't want to improve. It means that you are gentle with yourself in the process of becoming the parent that you want to be.

- Every time you feel guilty, take a pause and make a list of five things that you do super well as a parent. You can write them on a piece of paper or list them in your head.

- Start a gratitude journal. Every day, write in your journal one thing that you are grateful for and one nice moment that you and your child have enjoyed together.

- Ask your child's nursery or school to relay positives about their day via email or the home diary.

Key reminders

- Guilt serves no one.

- You *are* good enough.

- Guilt is totally self-inflicted, so it's time to stop enabling it.

- Be kind to yourself.

5
Connecting With Yourself And Others

In this chapter, you will:

- Understand why the most important person to connect with is *yourself*

- Learn how I connected with myself

- Explore some strategies to help you connect with yourself

- Learn how your behaviour may be impacting your partner

- Connect with your partner

- Connect with your family

- Understand what obstacles may be standing in the way of you connecting with your child

- Connect with your child's teachers and other professionals

Who is the most important person to connect with? Your partner? Your child? Your friends? The school teacher?

None of the above. The most important person to connect with is *you*. You need to have a full cup or, in my case, sometimes a full jug. Be resilient and have all the tools you need to look after yourself before you can even think about starting the journey with your conundrum kiddo.

The CAN approach is an integrated concurrent process – connection flows into achievement flows into navigation flows into connection. When a child connects with their environment, the people around them, and him or herself, they can achieve so much.

Just as the CAN approach applies to children, it also applies to parents. We must connect with those around us so that we can achieve a sense of wholeness and belonging, which will make navigating our journey a little bit easier.

Connecting with myself

Shortly after my brother unexpectedly passed away in January 2018 and I missed his funeral by hours, with him being Muslim and having to be buried in a tight timeframe, and me travelling for twenty-four hours back to South Africa, I became very depressed. I had started finding life difficult several months before but had simply carried on. Now I could no longer cope.

I was meant to be a successful businesswoman, founder of one of the leading paediatric occupational therapy practices in the area, so there was no time for admitting to being tired. For admitting to feeling insecure and inadequate. For not socialising with school mums and friends. For not enjoying my success. For the social anxieties which paralysed me.

My amazing husband and I were more disconnected than ever. Seemingly, we were going out with friends, having a good time, drinking (probably too much), yet we were not chatting anymore. My self-esteem plummeted and I took to my bed after work and at weekends, too exhausted to physically do anything else.

My amazing neighbour and friend recognised the signs of depression and encouraged me to see the GP. I cried (I love a good cry) and listened to the wonderful doctor reel off everything I was achieving while having been through what I had in my life. I admitted feeling weak about the prospect of taking antidepressants – I mean, the stigma, right?

She simply said, 'If you have a headache, you take a tablet. Your brain's chemical imbalance is making your whole body and life ache, so why not take a tablet?' I ended up having to take three, and they literally saved my life, my marriage and my practice.

During couples counselling, I realised that it was ridiculous of me to expect to be the most important person in my husband's life. He had to put himself first, just as I had to put myself and my well-being first, so that I could give as much as I was trying to give to others. To him, to my boys, to my siblings, to my friends, to my clients.

Until I felt well again (thank you, fluoxetine) and realised that I had neglected myself, I could simply not give anything to anyone. I started doing little things like using moisturiser (I know, I know – I should have been doing this all my life, not in my early forties), going for walks without listening to music and smiling at fellow dog walkers, reading (not just tribunal reports, but silly laugh-out-loud books), and being kind to myself by sitting down and having a meal which didn't consist of the boys' leftovers on their used plates.

I started feeling connected to myself. Which meant that I could give connection to others.

I wrote an email to my lovely therapists, telling them what I had gone through and the counselling I was having. Putting it out there, saying, 'Hey, guys, it may shock you, but I am actually not perfect.' And something wonderful happened – I then connected with my team and my practice in a way I hadn't done before. A way I *couldn't* do before, and it was life changing. That was a turning point for my practice.

Find ways to connect with and appreciate yourself. Buy yourself some flowers. Tell yourself how awesome you are (because you are). Put moisturiser on. Acknowledge your feelings. Admit when you feel low or flat and take action. Put yourself first.

It is absolutely not self-indulgent; it is a necessity that you owe to yourself and your family. But mostly, yourself. Sometimes, unfairly, families who have conundrum kids have to be strong and manage far more hurdles than others. Ultimately, self-care is a blessing.

Strategies to connect with yourself

You may like to use these strategies to help you feel calmer, more content and happier:

Breathe deeply

This takes practice. My breathing style usually consisted of either hyperventilating or holding my breath. Now I stop when I am feeling overwhelmed and take a deep breath into my belly, hold it for a few seconds, and then let go. This has really affected my decision making and reduced how I catastrophise when something minor happens.

Try it now. Breathe in through your nose for four counts, hold it for four counts, breathe out for eight counts.

Acknowledge your feelings

During my sessions with the best counsellor/magician/therapist in the world, I realised that my feelings are real. Hiding them or pushing them away doesn't serve me. So now, when I'm stressed, or overwhelmed, or feel like I'm about to lose it, I breathe deeply. Then I acknowledge that the current situation is rubbish, but I immediately find something to be grateful for. It honestly works.

Practise gratitude

I never used to understand the whole 'be grateful' malarkey until I tried it for myself. Now when I am really stressed and find it difficult to concentrate or fall asleep, I do an A–Z of things I'm grateful for, except I don't always start at A.

For example, I may start with F for friends, G for garden, H for home, I for internet, J for jelly babies, K for kids I work with (and my own, of course), L for life, etc. By pausing to think of specific things I'm grateful for, I usually come up with so many other things.

Don't listen to the news too much

The news causes unnecessary background noise which your mind does not need. I personally listen to podcasts rather than the radio when I'm driving – I wish I had started doing this earlier in my life. My favourites are ones related to entrepreneurship, business, self-awareness, self-actualisation and sometimes parenting.

Enjoy your own company

Do what you love – for me, it's walking, listening and dancing to country music, sewing, going to the gym (but only using the sauna, steam room and Jacuzzi), and reading. I enjoy feeling serene. Make time for yourself, be kind to yourself and smile.

Connecting with your partner

I had not realised how much seeing me in a dark place was affecting my husband. He loves me so much that he couldn't tell me how devastating it was to see me become someone I was not.

Outwardly, everyone thought we were on the same page. He suggested couples counselling, and at first,

I felt like a complete and utter failure. We had been married for almost twenty years – why should we need counselling? We should just get each other, right?

It was exactly because we had been together for so long and had both grown and evolved and changed (thank goodness), that we needed to work at our relationship. And the simplest way to connect would be to talk to each other. Simple. Just talk to each other.

I recall going out for dinner and watching other couples, some of them chatting and engaging and laughing, others barely able to make eye contact, let alone small talk. We used to say how that would never be us – how we would always talk to each other and communicate. How foolish we were to think that spending our lives with the same person would simply continue to be hunky-dory, without the need to work at it or go through rough patches.

Going for counselling was hard. Super hard, but also the best decision we ever made. It made me realise that our connection was still strong. And that any relationship needs constant work and honesty.

Sometimes, this is easier said than done. Trust me, I know. There are still moments where I find myself having a hard day and wanting to shut the door, but now, I say, 'I've had a shitty day. I want you to know, but I don't want you to do anything about it.' And that is fine.

I've recently started telling Zayn what level my tolerance battery is at: 'Just to let you know, I'm running at about 20% this morning.' Then he knows to stay out of my way. And I've also learned that just as I don't always want to talk, or I do want to rant, so does my dear husband.

There are many things you can do to connect with your partner. It doesn't have to be expensive or outrageous. I recently bonded with Zayn over a ridiculous reality TV show involving superyachts, rich people and the shenanigans of the crew. Being self-employed, we often work at night and can't always get into a serious series, so this was fun.

Connecting with your friends and family

I am fortunate to have a handful of good friends. When I say good friends, I mean the ones I can call at 2am and say, 'I need you', and they'll say, 'I'm on my way'.

But when I was struggling, I was too disconnected to hassle them with my woes. Why would they want to hear how hard I was finding not being able to connect with Xavier? How embarrassing to say, 'Man, I'm struggling so much that some days I cancel my first session because I physically can't get up.' I saw less and less of my core group of friends and started doing a lot of the Mummy juice – aka gin. And goodness me, did I gain some new friends. Wow, I was suddenly so popular. A cocktail Instagram page. A huge gin collection. Always out socialising. But more disconnected than ever.

MY EXPERIENCE

My dear friend, who I have known for years, came by one night and did her 'thing', which is like magic. She sat and listened. Like I had apparently done so many times for her, reassuring her that her kiddos were OK, and she didn't need to feel guilty.

Now it was my turn. I suddenly remembered what real connection felt like. And it didn't involve nights out partying; it involved a deep understanding, a raw honesty, exposing myself and saying, 'I'm really not OK. I feel like a failure.' And it was possible to do this without wine or gin.

Of course, this revelation was met in the nicest possible way by my friend: a derisive snort, followed by, 'You are one of the most inspiring, successful women I know. You're always there for everyone. Thank God you're not perfect. Thank goodness you remembered I'm always here for you, too.' And I felt like a deflating balloon, but in a good way. I was with my true friend.

When I was sitting in my favourite café, Wags and Tales, with a woman I'd met at ante-natal group in 2001, and I numbly, but quite matter-of-factly, told her what I had been keeping to myself, her reaction was a bit more jarring. And it is one of the reasons I love her so much. That's my honest, no-nonsense friend.

'Why the hell did you not say anything? Jesus, woman, what is wrong with you? Don't you know how much we love you? I'm furious you kept this from me.' She then sent a message to my poor old husband, giving him, in her words, 'a bollocking' for not calling her. We reconnected over cake and coffee, and goodness me, I love her to death.

Friends, and even acquaintances, just want the honest you. I don't mean moan about every little thing, that will become tedious for even your best friends, but when they ask how you are, they are usually genuinely interested.

The next time your friend says, 'How are you?', be honest. Be open. And at the same time, make yourself available to them. I've learned that sometimes I am so preoccupied with my own stuff, I cannot truly commit to listening to others. Put down your phone if you're together and just chat. Connect. Or if, like me, you have wonderful sisters in South Africa, or an awesome sister-in-law in Australia, pick up the phone and call them. Thank goodness for WhatsApp and Facetime.

Connecting with your child

The next step in connection is guiding your child to feel comfortable and safe enough to connect with those around them.

I personally struggled for a long time to connect with Xavier. I truly believe that his traumatic birth (you try pushing out an 11lb 11oz baby in the so-called 'natural way' and not being traumatised) really affected my attachment to him. Everything about the birth was horrifying. Then he had to be whisked away (because he was ginormous) while I crashed from the blood loss.

And my poor husband. I remember seeing his worried face, and his words: 'I had to take Xavier to the neonatal intensive care unit, not knowing if I would see you alive again.' Birth is traumatic for everyone involved, including the partners. When I am struggling as an OT to connect with one of the kids I am working with, or I'm finding it difficult to understand a parent-child relationship, I always ask the parent about the birth. Few people realise just how much childbirth can affect us.

MY EXPERIENCE

I went back to work when Xavier was just a couple of months old, having no issues leaving him with Zayn. I remember seeing the health visitor and doing the postnatal depression checklist, then she asked me to see the GP.

Noah's birth couldn't have been more different from Xavier's. The consultant wanted to do a caesarean, and I said, 'Hell, yes!' Noah had already been measured as big, and so the consultant agreed to deliver him two weeks early.

We had to wait until the end of the day so that all the specialists could be present – they didn't want a repeat of last time. I chose some lovely music, and the entire procedure was absolutely delightful. I can clearly remember how I felt when Noah was shown to me. I bonded with him instantly.

I tried really hard to connect with Xavier. I love him to death, but my postnatal depression meant that not only did I find all of life's daily tasks torturous, I also found it hard to form a bond with him. And all my relationships suffered. As Xavier started showing more signs of struggling and needing help with transitions, I became more and more in denial, and this really shut me off.

I tried to find answers everywhere. Maths groups, martial arts, ballet classes, football, rugby – you name it, and I signed him up for it to find what he was good at. I tried to find out what he was comfortable with and what he would be happy doing with other children.

But he cried and resisted going because he couldn't do crowds. He couldn't do social interaction. He couldn't read the other kids. I felt more and more powerless, guilty and inadequate.

Attachment is something that I find fascinating. I wish I knew more about it, but what I do know is that I don't know enough. There are several articles about childbirth and how it affects your attachment

– I never knew that some women can experience Post Traumatic Stress Disorder from childbirth.[4]

The four attachment styles

There are four child/adult attachment styles:[5/6]

Secure – autonomous

The adults in these relationships are generally comfortable in themselves. They don't avoid getting close to others or letting others get close to them, and have no difficulties depending on others and having others depend on them. They have little anxiety and generally don't worry about being rejected because they are secure in their relationships.

Generally speaking, infants and kids who regularly get their needs met, including love and attention, tend to have secure attachments. These kids are confident, have strong boundaries, communicate well and are OK with trying what they are not good at.

---

4   A L MacKinnon, S Houazene, S Robins, N Feeley, P Zelkowitz 'Maternal attachment style, interpersonal trauma history, and childbirth-related post-traumatic stress', *Frontiers in Psychology*, 28 November 2018, https://dx.doi.org/10.3389%2Ffpsyg.2018.02379

5   C E Ackerman, 'What is attachment theory? Bowlby's four stages explained', *Positive Psychology*, 15 April 2020, www.positivepsychology.com/attachment-theory

6   K Spears, S Chupein, 'Understanding different types of attachment', Better Help, 29 July 2020, www.betterhelp.com/advice/attachment/understanding-different-types-of-attachment

Avoidant – dismissing

The adults in these relationships tend to avoid intimacy, closeness and dependence on others. They have little anxiety and don't worry about whether their partners are available or not. Trusting others is hard for them and they are fiercely independent. Infants in these relationships only have some of their needs met, eg they get fed and cleaned regularly, but don't get held or hugged often.

Anxious – preoccupied

Anxiety levels are sky high for these adults and they are insecure about their relationships. They crave emotional and physical closeness.

When a baby/child grows up in unpredictable circumstances with an anxious parent, they tend to be anxious too. Sometimes all their needs are met, other times none or only some of them are met. They generally think better of their peers than they do of themselves.

Disorganised – unresolved

Avoidant adults shy away from intimacy and worry about another person's love and commitment. As children, they tend to have grown up in horrible circumstances. They really struggle to relate to their friends, sometimes wanting to be close and other times not.

My attachment style was definitely anxious. For more about your own attachment style and how it affects your parenting, start by reading Lisa Firestone PhD's blog post, 'How your attachment style affects your parenting'.[7]

CASE STUDY – SAMUEL

Jane had brought her son Samuel to see me. He struggled with sensory difficulties, including noise sensitivity, as well as difficulties with food textures.

Jane was onboard and engaged in Sam's therapy. Over weeks of chatting during therapy sessions, she told me her husband, Tony, was finding it difficult to engage with Sam. Sam couldn't tolerate the sound of Tony's voice, and Tony only seemed to interact with Sam at dinner time, raising his voice, telling him to eat. This caused Sam to cover his ears and scream, which of course caused more shouting from Tony.

Jane tried to make Tony see that raising his voice wasn't the way to deal with Sam and that they both needed to be patient. They clearly weren't on the same page, and this was causing a rift between them. I suggested that perhaps Tony bring Sam to his next session.

---

7   L Firestone, 'How your attachment style affects your parenting', *Psychology Today* blog, 19 October 2015, www.psychologytoday.com/gb/blog/compassion-matters/201510/how-your-attachment-style-affects-your-parenting

I had met Tony at Sam's initial assessment. He was clearly an intelligent, high-achieving man who ran his own company. He also loved his son to bits.

When they arrived, Sam went through our usual routine of taking off his coat, hanging it on the peg and putting his shoes next to mine. We went into the room, where Sam proceeded to make a list of the session's activities using pictures. Tony sat awkwardly on one of the little chairs and looked out of place.

As we went through the session, I did my usual narration, telling Tony why we were doing certain activities. When Sam asked for the big swinging song, I became embarrassed as it involved me singing (bear in mind that I should not sing, not even in the shower).

Tony looked at me quizzically and said, 'He hates singing and noise.' I shrugged and positioned Sam on his tummy in the net swing, gave him my hands, and he held on. I started singing and Sam squealed with delight.

Sam then looked at Tony, who had moved onto the floor with us, and said, 'Daddy, sing! Sing!' And Tony sang. Almost as badly as I did, but sing he did.

While we carried on the session, Tony told me how hard he had been finding connecting with Sam. His daughter was as neurotypical as they came. She was as delightful as Sam, but also different. She had great conversations with Tony and they had a strong relationship, while Sam was wary of his 6 foot 5 inch ex-rugby player dad. And when Tony raised his voice out of frustration, Sam shut down.

Tony explained that he had now realised how much his son needed routines and how important Sam's sensitivities were to his day-to-day emotional regulation. I set Tony a challenge – to count to ten every time he felt like shouting, and instead think what Sam was struggling with.

Tony started verbalising to the family, but mainly to himself, what Sam was finding hard, and it made all the difference. I didn't tell Tony to do this – he said that he often found himself talking through his day in his mind, then he did it out loud one day and Sam visibly calmed down. Tony had naturally transitioned from an avoidant to a secure attachment style, and as a result, he and his son connected.

Connecting with teachers and other professionals

There are few things as frustrating as not feeling understood or heard by teachers and professionals. And it's easy to say, 'Stay calm. Work with them. Explain things', but sometimes, you have to lose your shit and go full-on mamma-bear. I'm not proud of when I've had to do this, but all my boys have is my husband and me. We are their advocates.

Quite often, our kids are connected to their teaching staff, support assistants or classroom helpers. And often, this can cause parents to feel a bit out of the loop, or even slightly jealous. To these parents, I say, 'How lucky you are to know your child is so well cared for, so well connected to another adult, that they are happy and comfortable until they are back in your care.'

Be honest with teachers. Tell them you feel like you're being ignored or not listened to. And be realistic. Listen to them. Most teachers only want what is best for your child.

Key reminders

- Your mental health is important – this is not self-indulgent, but a fact.

- Admitting you need help takes courage, but it's well worth doing. Don't struggle on alone.

- Needing medication is not a sign of failure.

- Make sure you and your partner continue to take an interest in each other.

- Be honest with your partner. Listen without judgement.

- Not everything is your fault – if your partner is having a bad day, it is not for you to fix.

- Be honest with your friends and family. There is huge power in a quick text message simply saying, 'Thinking of you – how are things?'

- Childbirth can be incredibly traumatic – seek professional help if you find yourself unable to forget events surrounding your child's birth.

- Partners can be deeply affected by a traumatic birth, too.

- What is your attachment style? What were your parents' attachments styles? Did they change over the years?

- Question whether how you communicate with your child is helping or hindering them.

- Be honest with your child's teachers and other professionals and listen to what they have to say.

6
Ways To Connect

In this chapter, you will:

- Learn how coming to terms with your child's additional needs can be akin to bereavement

- Realise the power of daily connections

- Discover the fun of saying yes – to everything

- Connect through play

- Learn the valuable role animals can play in connecting with the conundrum child

I was a very different person, pre-kids. I was judgy and knew it all – even about parenting, despite not being one. I was one who said, 'When I have kids…'

After I had kids, things changed. I now explain it to the ones who don't have kids on my therapy team like this.

When you're pregnant, you have hopes and dreams. You imagine what your little baby will be like, what they will grow up to be. No one ever thinks about the possibility of autism, a cleft palate, cerebral palsy, ADHD or a brain injury. And I genuinely believe that when your child has these difficulties, you go through a bereavement.

Elisabeth Kübler-Ross's denial, anger, bargaining, depression and acceptance (DABDA) grief model really resonates with me.[8] As part of my occupational therapy degree, when I did a mental health module, including a variation of the model with the acronym DANDA (we used negotiating instead of bargaining), I thought back to when my mum told me that my dad had killed himself. I had gone straight into D – denial. He would never have done this – he loved me. Surely it was a mistake, an accident.

Then came the A – I was angry. Someone must have killed him – a dealer; one of his junkie friends; his new girlfriend. I was angry with my mother for not giving him another chance, for divorcing him. I was angry with myself for not going to visit him. Negotiation,

---

8   E Kübler-Ross, *On Death and Dying: What the dying have to teach doctors, nurses, clergy and their own families* (Scribner Book Company, reprint edition 2014)

depression and acceptance only came with time for me.

When Xavier was young, I was in denial about autism and Asperger syndrome. I was angry that my son couldn't interact or transition easily. I was furious that teachers didn't get him. I hated that he needed medication to sleep and would be exhausted most days. I was livid that he wouldn't wear normal socks. I was genuinely upset that he didn't like parties – not even his own. And I was devastated that I couldn't connect with him.

I negotiated – good lord, did I negotiate and bargain. With teachers, my husband, myself, the paediatricians, the psychiatrist, and poor Xavier. I guess the depression was pretty obvious – hence the fluoxetine.

And then, after a long time, came acceptance. Not the superficial acceptance of buying uber-expensive seamless socks and washing new bedding twice before putting it on his bed. Not acceptance where I gave up asking him to stop wearing jumpers in the summer. I am referring to the acceptance that comes from ugly sleepless nights of crying, screaming and yelling, reading sleep studies, tactile defensiveness and trying all sorts of treatments (because even at my most rational, I thought I could magic autism away – not my proudest moment). The true acceptance came from the wonderful quiet time. Just the two of us reading or crafting, or me watching him be absolutely delighted at digging a hole in the garden, writing copious little letters and notes, building the most amazing Lego and Meccano structures, and drawing so beautifully.

Our life became so much better when I accepted him. I stopped asking, 'Do you want to have a birthday party?' except when it was as a joke just before the big one-eight. Oh, how we laughed! And how we laughed when we suggested to Noah that they should have a joint sixteenth and eighteenth, because Noah is just as crowd averse as Xavier, and *very* sound sensitive.

I tell the parents I work with all these little stories because that's my way of connecting with them. Of letting them know that they are not alone. That their confusion, questions and worries are all a valid part of their journey. Their frustrations are real. Because I know that one tiny little connection will be a weight off their shoulders, like it was for me when I found a kindred spirit to speak to. And that will be the start of their connection with others.

Connecting is about learning, having fun while achieving and navigating. You CAN do it!

Daily connections

I have a list up in the clinic of 'Things to ask the kids after school'. I used to pick the boys up, madly dashing to the unauthorised late club, and found that when

I said, 'How was your day?' they would say, 'OK' and shrug. Every. Single. Day.

Then I found online lists of questions to ask kids about their day, and suddenly things changed. Specific questions relating to detentions and other boys being sent to the headmaster's office always led to detailed discussions.

My top ten afterschool questions:

- Who made you laugh?

- Which teacher was silly?

- Who got into trouble and why?

- What did you have for lunch?

- Did anyone or anything make you feel sad/ angry?

- Did you do anything you are/are not proud of?

- Who was kind?

- Did anyone play on their own?

- Who lost privilege/golden time or got detention? (I am very nosey, OK?)

- What was the worst lesson?

My best moments of connection have been unplanned, spontaneous, and often silly and engaging.

Connect by saying yes

One of the best ways I have found of connecting with conundrum kids is to say yes to everything. For one hour, or maybe even a whole morning, I encourage parents and friends to try this. It is so much fun and your kids will think you're awesome.

Pick a random day during the holidays or on the weekend. Be warned – you will be exhausted, and you won't get your chores done, but you will connect with your child.

Here are some of the things I said yes to:

- Yes, we can have breakfast for lunch
- Yes, I will watch your dance-off
- Yes, we can play Simon Says again (for the fifth time today)
- Yes, you can play 'Baby Shark' at volume 10
- Yes, you can ask Alexa to tell you jokes

Saying yes all the time is not only impractical, but it could make your children feel entitled, and no one wants that. You still have things to do – the dinner to cook, the toilet to clean – but you can put that off for a morning of yes fun. The chores will still be there, waiting for you tomorrow (or, if the toilet is really gross, after the kids have gone to bed). But these moments of connection won't be there all the time.

Saying yes to older kids and teenagers is also something I suggest you do – more about that in the Navigation section.

Connect through being playful

One of my go-to suggestions for parents to let go of guilt and connect is to take time (even five minutes) to play with their kids and have fun. This is something so worth practising – play to connect. I will say it again – play to connect. Not because you feel you have to (eg playing an educational game to teach certain skills), but to laugh and enjoy being with each other. I have found my own happiness levels go through the roof when I let go and have fun.

Try these tips for being more playful:

- Be available – a connected parent always makes time for play. Leave your chores or, in my case, reports and invoices, and let your kids know you are choosing them over everything else. Even if it's only for five minutes, they will feel valued, you will have fun, and it's a good way to destress.

- Devices away – start with ten minutes of screen-free time. Tablets, phones, gadgets all go on a shelf, and that includes your own. A quick game of *It* or *What's the time, Mr Wolf?* gets everyone up and about. For older kids, I suggest *Bananagrams* or *Dobble*.

- Be enthusiastic – if you're going to play or read or build, then do it like it is the most exciting thing you have ever done. Noah used to collect stones, and the joy in his little face when I was super enthusiastic about his collection, asking him questions and choosing my favourite one, was priceless. By being excited, you inject energy and joy into your playful interactions, and give your child the sense that being passionate about something is amazing. Which it is.

- Focus. Be present – be in that moment with them. Whether you're building a Lego stegosaurus or talking about the latest Forex updates (my fifteen-year-old's obsession), go with it. I have no clue about Forex, but Noah loves explaining it to me. It's his chosen topic, so I let him direct our interaction.

- Be silly – playful parents forget their age and join their kids in fun. Be creative, let your imagination run wild, dance, act or sing. Just be silly.

Animals

In my work, I have found that animals are wonderful at connecting with conundrum children. Before I introduced Buster to being a 'therapy' dog, I used to joke and say that he was too hyperactive to be of any use. The first child he encountered was anxious and also hyperactive, but Buster sat down, tilted his head, and the little boy stopped and looked at him. He then stroked Buster gently, while his mum and I watched this interaction between boy and dog in amazement.

CASE STUDY – JAIMIE AND BUSTER

Jaimie was an incredibly bright fifteen-year-old girl attending a selective grammar school, where she was usually top of her class. She was preparing to take her GCSEs and was predicted to do very well.

In the process of studying under all the pressure the expectations put on her, Jaimie had become fraught with anxiety. She had started avoiding school and had missed a number of days. She had initially come to occupational therapy about a year previously to work on strategies for improving her study technique and executive functioning. Her mum emailed me and asked if there was anything we could do now as she was concerned about Jaimie's mental health. We arranged a day, and I hoped that her mum would get Jaimie to the clinic.

They arrived on a Wednesday afternoon, as Buster, my hyperactive Bug (a cross between a Pug and Boston Terrier), and I had just returned from a quick walk. I knew Jaimie was wary around dogs, despite claiming to like them. But before I could put Buster behind the stair gate, he had gone and sniffed Jaimie's shoes, and then started licking them (he is a weird dog).

Jaimie squealed and smiled. I apologised and went to pick him up, but she said, 'Can I play with him?'

Her mum and I were both stunned, and I hesitantly said yes. Buster had never done anything more than letting the kids stroke him after their sessions, wagging his curly tail, much to their delight. I was conscious that many kids were scared of dogs, so carefully controlled who would and wouldn't see or come into contact with Buster, even if just accidentally.

We stayed in the waiting room and watched as Buster, tired from his umpteenth walk that day, lay by Jaimie's feet. She sat on the floor and Buster climbed onto her lap. Her initial reaction was a little gasp, her arms and hands retracted, but she almost instantaneously put her hands on his back and started stroking him. We were amazed. And Buster got his first paying client.

Over the next few weeks, Jaimie went to a class in the morning, and in the afternoon saw Buster. With breathing and mindfulness exercises, she had become much calmer. She started taking Buster for walks with me, we became regulars in our local doggy café, and the transformation in both the girl and dog was astonishing. Her anxiety and wariness around animals had reduced significantly, and her confidence had grown following her 'training' of Buster – he listened to her and did what she asked, which was a wonderful boost for her.

Jaimie's teachers and parents noticed a big difference. They also took on board how much pressure they had inadvertently put on Jaimie (simply saying how proud they were of her and how well she was doing had been anxiety inducing for her). The school implemented regular relaxation sessions for all the girls in Year 11, and most girls downloaded either Calm or Headspace onto their mobiles. And Jaimie and Buster remain each other's biggest fans to this day.

Key reminders

- Understand that you may go through the five stages of grief, as first outlined by Elisabeth Kübler-Ross, before you can fully accept your conundrum child.

- Don't just ask your child how their day went. Connect on a daily basis by asking specific questions that will get them talking.

- Be playful and present with your child.

- Try saying yes to everything, just for a morning (but not forever).

- If you have animals in your home, or access to animals elsewhere, don't underestimate the connection they can have with the conundrum child.

7
Anxiety

In this chapter, you will:

- Recognise what may be making your child anxious

- Allow your child to find their own ways to connect with others

- Understand that your child's behaviour may be an expression of their anxiety

- Hear from an expert on how to help your child overcome the 'worry monster'

- Confront the elephant in the room: bullying

Anxiety is one of the greatest difficulties kids with additional needs face. They are different. They may not have anxieties as we know it. They may. It is prudent to bear in mind that they are confused, worried, scared and overwhelmed – all things we as parents feel.

Anxiety is debilitating. If I was clever enough, I would write books about the awful effects of anxiety. But for now, I'll simply say that connecting with the anxious child can literally be life changing for them.

Help your anxious child connect with others

As parents, we are our child's voice. We are their advocates. We guide them. And often, we have to guide others to make the connection and understand our child. But not always.

MY EXPERIENCE

I used to be obsessed with inviting other kids for playdates so that the boys could interact with children other than each other. But Xavier had particular interests. And sometimes, they made no sense to other kids.

I remember one day, Xavier's friend arrived, and I shouted for Xavier to come inside. He didn't, and so Todd went out to the garden. I prepared myself for Todd to come back inside and play with Noah, the cats or the train set – anything but Xavier.

As I waited for him to come back inside (yes, I left the boys for two minutes on their own – shock/horror), I realised that I could hear little chatting voices. I went outside and found that Xavier had been digging – we didn't have a show garden, and I firmly believe every garden should have a digging area. Usually, his friends would stare at him in horror, but not Todd. He had simply found another little spade and sat on his haunches, digging with Xavier.

This little boy had connected with Xavier. He had engaged in an activity with Xavier and found a way in. I realised that I had been so worried about sheltering Xavier and having him fit into other's lives, I'd never given anyone a chance to truly connect with him.

I am fortunate at my practice to have some amazing equipment. Often, when kids are playing or swinging or lying under hundreds of balls, they will tell me things, completely unprompted, that are shockingly revealing.

These revelations have included:

- Why can't I understand the schoolwork? I wish my brain worked.

- I hate how my socks feel, but I couldn't move in class because the teacher said to sit still.

- Why is it so noisy in the dining room? I can't eat at school.

- I can't keep up with my friends. Do you think they like me?

- I don't understand why there was a different escort on the bus today. I'm really worried Ruth won't be back. I like Ruth. She never touches my hair.

Many kids will exhibit anxieties through their behaviours – hiding, withdrawing, crying, self-injurious behaviours stemming from a sensory regulation need, hitting, lashing out, shouting or being disruptive. These behaviours make it clear to everyone the child is not coping.

Then there are kids who, for want of a better word, are 'perfect' at school. But the minute they see the person/s who grounds them and carries them and truly gets them, they have a meltdown. Teachers often do not believe parents, as much as they want to. They can't believe that sweet little Manny could hurt anyone, let alone his mum and dad. They can't believe that the bruise on his little sister's arm is from him. And so they assume he is fine.

Once we as parents have an open, connected dialogue with the school, friends and therapists or tutors, we can all approach our child consistently. And this in itself reduces any anxiety, leaving our child feeling safe and happy, available to learn and make more connections.

I believe that one of the biggest factors in true connection is raw honesty. If you don't tell your partner/ husband/ best friend/ son's teacher/ daughter's behaviour support assistant exactly how you feel and what your goals are, you may never be on the same page as them, and this disconnect will be most obvious to your child. And however small or insignificant this may seem, it will cause anxiety for your child.

Be honest and realistic when you think about what you really want for your child. Is it to go to an Oxbridge or Russell Group University, get a degree, get a top-paying job, buy a house and travel? Or is it to take the opportunities they come across, be independent, contribute to their community and be happy?

Ultimately, Zayn and I just want our kids to be happy. We want our kids to be independent, ideally move out sometime before they're thirty-five (fat chance in today's economy), have a career which makes them happy and is fulfilling, give back to their community and be kind. The world doesn't need any more arrogant jerks; it needs more kindness. We can never have enough kindness.

The worry monster

So many of the children I see are referred to me because their debilitating anxiety is stopping them from doing the activities they want to do which would allow them independence and happiness. I have had the pleasure of working with Giselle Monbiot, who is a specialist in stress and anxiety management, guiding individuals and groups to overcome the hurdles that they might face in their professional and personal life. She runs workshops for parents to learn how they can support their anxious child and themselves through this challenging time, or works directly with children/teenagers for a more in-depth bespoke approach.

Here she shares her approach to reducing the worry monster.

EXPERT VIEW – A SIMPLE APPROACH TO HELPING CHILDREN WITH STRESS AND ANXIETY

The number of young people looking for help with stress and anxiety is on the increase. Parents want to support and help their child and can become anxious themselves as they attempt to understand what they can do.

Stress and anxiety in children express themselves in a number of ways. Some examples of anxiety expressed in younger children can be complaints of aches and pains in the body and stomach; clinging to parents; not wanting to be alone; anger or struggling at bedtime. Examples for older children are complaints of headaches, or a change in sleeping, eating and social patterns.

Instinctively, parents understand that the key to helping children through stress and anxiety is early intervention, but they have no idea where to start with this. They may chat to the school or their GP but realise that any professional intervention can take months to put in place. There are many children experiencing mild to moderate anxiety who, if they're helped promptly and effectively, can learn how to respond more calmly and feel more confident with life's challenges. The earlier they are helped, the less likely it is the anxiety will become severe.

I now want to share a series of powerful techniques to reduce stress that benefit both young children and teenagers – the parent just needs to tweak the language to make it age-appropriate. If they're practised regularly, they can reduce anxiety levels. While your child is learning the techniques, practise them when they're calm, rather than in a heightened state of anxiety.

Three steps to reducing the worry monster:

1) Body scan and muscle tensing. Starting with your toes, clench them for two seconds and let go. Then your feet: clench and let go. Then your calves: clench and let go. Continue up your body, clenching different parts to the top of your head, including your face. This releases any stress stored in the muscles.

2) Five deep breaths in and out. Inhale deeply through your nose, breathing down to the stomach, and exhale through the mouth. Do the breaths slowly and powerfully. Repeat five times. This helps to relax the body and mind as it reduces adrenaline build-up and enables the brain to become more coherent.

3) Visualise a happy memory. Make the colours as bright as you can. What can you see around you, both close by and in the distance? What was it about the experience

that made it such a happy one? Connect into the feelings of happiness. Where do you feel that feeling? Focus on it and let it grow. Now you can go to this place anytime you wish.

Our thoughts create how we feel, so if we are thinking stressed thoughts, we will feel stressed. If we revisit a happy memory, then the feelings of joy, gratitude or connection will manifest. This helps reset the brain and body. The feelings of stress either disappear or reduce, making it easier to see the situation in a more rational way.

Take time to do this with your child. The connection you both experience while sharing the practice will create a deep emotional attachment. This in itself is healing. With younger children, include the practice in your bedtime routine. With older children, find the time to connect emotionally, and then speak through the sequence when they are open to your suggestions.

Bullying and being mean

Kids can be mean. And I've encountered many mean parents, too.

MY EXPERIENCE

I was bullied at primary school and high school for the bad stutter I had. It was horrendous. I was bullied and teased because my dad was an alcoholic. I was teased for pretending that ketchup on bread was my favourite lunch, when in fact it was obvious, we couldn't afford anything else.

I was born during the Apartheid – a political and social system during the era of white minority rule in South Africa. It enforced racial discrimination against non-whites, mainly focused on skin colour and facial features. The private high school I went to was predominantly attended by black kids who were quite politically active and outspoken.

When Nelson Mandela was released, our school shut while we went dancing in the streets. This was great and I loved it, but I lived in a 'coloured' township. And because of segregation, we even classed ourselves. Everyone thought they were better than the next person. I remember getting the bus to school and the so-called coloured children would throw rocks and stones and empty drinks cans at the handful of us for going to school with black kids.

My kids were teased for, among other things, wearing glasses, having afro hair, not liking sports, wanting to wear jumpers all year round, struggling with reading, being overweight, hating sleepovers and being good at maths. I always said to them, 'Kids are mean because they worry about themselves. Just make sure that whenever you see someone else struggling, at least say hello to them. No matter how annoying they may be, we don't know what they are struggling with.'

As parents, we need to be careful about what we say in front of our kids because they copy us and learn from us. If we say to another mum or our partner, 'Gosh, I saw Jodie have a meltdown today. She is so rude and annoying', is it a surprise that our child tells Jodie, 'You're so rude and annoying. I don't want to play with you'? Jodie then starts thinking and believing that there is something wrong with her. Her self-esteem and confidence plummet.

When kids come to me for an assessment, I ask them these questions:

- What are you good at?

- What makes you happy?

- What do you struggle with?

- What do you want to get better at (which is not always the thing they struggle with)?

- What makes you sad? Often, the answer is 'When kids tease me, are mean to me or bully me' or 'When other kids don't want to be friends with me'.

- What do you want to be when you grow up?

I love this part of the assessment because the answers are so pure. And I usually get to feel really connected to the kids. If parents are in the room listening in, sometimes they tut, smile or well up.

How heart-breaking that the one thing most kids are saddened by is related to feeling disconnected from their peers. To not being understood or accepted.

When a child is really struggling at school and teachers ask me for ideas or advice, we work with the kids in the class to make an 'About me' poster. Each child gets to stand up and answer the above questions to the class. This is such a lovely and revealing exercise. Kids being honest with each other is humbling. And more often than not, it connects some of the most unlikely kids.

Key reminders

- Anxiety can manifest itself in a number of different ways.

- Constantly asking someone if they are anxious or worried can make them more anxious and worried.

- Practise what you preach – if you're feeling anxious, verbalise it, and then narrate your strategy.

- Have an open dialogue with everyone your child comes into contact with to make sure you are all connecting with them in a consistent way. This can go a long way to reducing your child's anxiety.

- Use the powerful techniques for reducing stress as shared by Giselle in her case study.

- Remember, and encourage your child to remember, that bullying is often due to anxiety. Be kind.

- Watch how you behave. Even when you think no one is looking, kids are always listening and watching, and they will copy you.

PART THREE
ACHIEVE

8
Sensory Processing

In this chapter, you will:

- Get an overview of the foundational skills OTs work on

- Understand the importance of good sensory processing in everyday life

- Learn that we all have eight senses

- See how the tactile system provides information about the world

- Learn about the protective and discriminative tactile systems

- Consider the Wilbarger Deep Pressure and Proprioceptive Technique for approaching tactile hypersensitivity

- Define proprioception
- Learn about the vestibular system
- Take a look at auditory and visual difficulties

The *Cambridge English Dictionary* defines 'achieve' as 'to succeed in finishing something or reaching an aim, especially after a lot of work or effort; to do or obtain something that you wanted after planning and working to make it happen.'[9]

The *Oxford Learner's Dictionary* defines 'achieve' as '[transitive]: achieve something – to succeed in reaching a particular goal, status or standard, especially by making an effort for a long time.'[10]

When we achieve a goal with significant importance to us, it means we have worked really hard towards it and are proud of what we have achieved. Achieving our goals generally makes us feel successful and raises our self-esteem. I believe that all our conundrum kids are capable of achieving great things, but we need to make sure that their playing field is level. It is often the case that their underlying foundational skills are disordered, and so they are at a disadvantage compared to their peers.

---

9 Cambridge English Dictionary, www.dictionary.cambridge.org/dictionary/english/achieve
10 Oxford Learner's Dictionary, www.oxfordlearnersdictionaries.com/definition/english/achieve

The foundational skills include:

- Sensory processing
- Emotional regulation
- Motor skills
- Visual perception
- Executive function

In this part of the book, 'Achieve', we are going to explore what these foundational skills are, how they affect us when they aren't working well, and simple strategies we as parents can follow at home to make life a little easier and more enjoyable for our kids (and thus ourselves). This chapter will focus on sensory processing.

What is sensory processing disorder?

Pioneering OT and psychologist A Jean Ayres PhD likened sensory processing disorder (SPD) to a neurological traffic jam that prevents certain parts of the brain from receiving the information they need to interpret sensory information correctly.[11] I like this analogy and often describe SPD as a massive traffic jam where signals are delayed or traffic lights are not working correctly. This happens within the brain

---

11   'Understanding sensory processing disorder', www.spdstar.org/ basic/understanding-sensory-processing-disorder

when information that we receive through our senses results in abnormal or unusual responses.

Sensory processing is basically the way that our nervous system gets the messages from our senses and turns them into our responses or reactions. When you have SPD, the sensory information and stimuli go into your brain, but do not get organised into appropriate or correct responses. Sensory information gets confused in the brain, and so the responses are in themselves confusing. What you will find is that people with SPD will respond quite differently to other people.

There are two main areas of sensory processing. One is called sensory modulation and the other is called sensory discrimination. Sensory modulation is when we over- or under-respond to incoming stimuli from the environment. For example, I might perceive a small cut on my finger in such a way that the pain is overwhelming, and I feel like I need to go to the hospital. Sensory discrimination allows us to use our senses to get more particular and specific information about incoming stimuli. For example, I can put my hand into a pencil case and, simply by using my sense of touch, know whether I have picked up a pencil or a wax crayon.

In recent years, SPD has become one of the top reasons kids are referred to OTs. And it's one of the main reasons kids are dysregulated and struggle to engage. Excellent books to read on the subject include *Sensa-*

tional Kids by Lucy Jane Miller[12] and *The Out-of-Sync Child* by Carol Stock Kranowitz.[13]

The tactile system

We have eight senses (not five as most people commonly think) and difficulty processing any one of these senses can lead to a child being dysregulated. The eight senses (in case you are wondering) are touch, vision, hearing, smell, taste, movement, body awareness and interception.[14]

The tactile system provides information about the world, specifically about the shape, size and texture of objects. Tactile information helps us to understand our surroundings, to feel safe and to bond with loved ones. Not only does it underlie social, emotional, physiological and neurological development, but it also permits us to manipulate objects and use tools proficiently.

The tactile system has two parts: the protective system and the discriminative system. Both must work well separately and together.

---

12 LJ Miller, *Sensational Kids: Hope and help for children with sensory processing disorder* (Penguin Random House USA, 2014)
13 C Stock Kranowitz, *The Out-of-sync Child: Recognizing and coping with sensory processing disorder* (Pedigree, new edition 2005)
14 Staff contributor, 'The 8 senses: How your child interacts with the environment', Children's Home Society of Minnesota blog, 29 August 2018, www.chlss.org/blog/8-senses-parenting-sensory-processing-disorder

The protective system is critical for our basic safety and survival. This system will activate the classic 'fright-flight' responses, causing our bodies to respond with stress.

The discriminative system allows us to feel where we are touched and/or what we are touching. For example, we can put our hand in our pocket and select a penny from an assortment of change. Some indications that the discriminative system is not working efficiently are:

- A child may have poor fine motor skills

- They touch everything, or even lick objects

- They don't appear to notice a touch

- They don't notice when they are dirty

- They often drop things

- They have a high pain threshold – they bump themselves and fall over, but don't appear to be in pain

- They have a low pain threshold – every injury is 'major' to them

The vast majority of children I see have an over-responsive tactile system. These children may:

- Pull away from a light touch

- Dislike certain clothes or food

- Struggle to queue or line up

- Avoid getting dirty, messy play, art

- Be resistant to new tactile experiences

- Resist face/hair washing, nail cutting, dressing and undressing

Tactile defensiveness is one of the biggest barriers to development. This is where the protective system kicks in, alerting the child to perceived danger, causing a 'fight, flight, fright or freeze' response.

When I gave birth to the boys, the initial skin-to-skin touch was incredible, and so it was throughout their first few months and years – suckling, cuddling, stroking their cheeks, little kisses on their hands and feet, butterfly fairy kisses (you know the kind – blink and your eyelashes kiss their cheeks). Once they were older, it was a reassuring squeeze on their arm before they did something they were worried about. A little high five. A pat on the back. A ruffle of their hair.

Imagine you can't do that. Imagine your child finds light touch so distressing that they pull away. Imagine that every time you change their nappy, they scream because they perceive it as pain. Every time you buy new clothes, they have to be washed twice to make them feel just right. When you wash the bedding, your child needs to be prepared and warned about the big change. Imagine that when they can feel a seam of their sock rubbing against their toe, that is all they think about.

Being averse to light touch is one of the most common forms of SPD. These kiddos are constantly anxious. They live in fight or flight mode, worrying about their peers bumping into them, their teacher ruffling their hair, having to change for PE, putting their coats on, taking their coats off, not to mention the sheer horror of messy play. And in severe cases, tactile hypersensitivity can cause significant difficulties with eating and brushing their teeth. Watching your child refuse to eat or only eat certain foods is very distressing. But as distressing as it is for you, it is really exhausting and scary for kids.

If this describes your child, as much as possible:

- Avoid crowds

- Don't touch them lightly

- Don't touch them without warning

- Let them choose their own clothes

- Use firm touch

- Ask the teacher if the child can stand at the back of the line

The Wilbarger Deep Pressure and Proprioceptive Technique

One of the most useful treatment approaches I have personally found is the Wilbarger Deep Pressure and Proprioceptive Technique (DPPT), a sensory-based strategy.[15]/[16] I remember going on a training session with Patricia and Julia Wilbarger (mother and daughter). In a room filled with about 100 paediatric OTs, not one of us was doing it correctly, according to the Wilbargers. We were shocked, but none of us had actually been directly trained in this method.

When I prescribe DPPT, I let parents know that it is very intensive. Not only does every person who is going to be carrying out the brushing need to be directly trained by an OT, but they need to carry it out every one and a half to two hours during the child's waking day. It only takes three minutes, but it's hard.

DPPT is like taking antibiotics – you only stop once the course is finished, and in this case, I'd say give it two full weeks. Parents either go away and think about it and tell me that it's too much for them right now, or, if they are desperate, they want to start it immediately. About two in ten parents persist.

---

15 '10 realities of the OT brushing protocol', The Anonymous OT blog, nd, www.theanonymousot.com/2017/10/03/10-realities-of-the-ot-brushing-protocol

16 'Tactile overresponsivity (tactile defensiveness): So that's why he acts that way', The Sensory Processing Disorder (SPD) Resource Center blog, nd, www.sensory-processing-disorder.com/tactile-defensiveness.html

Do *not* use this approach if you have not been trained by your child's OT. Also, make sure the OT has had the correct training.

CASE STUDY – BEATRIX

Beatrix was a nervous-looking eight-year-old girl. When she first came to see me, it was freezing outside. In fact, it was snowing.

She arrived wearing thin trousers and a short-sleeved polo shirt. Her hair was unbrushed and she had no socks on. Her mum was carrying her coat and a bag containing her jumper, hat, gloves, scarf and socks. And her underwear. Beatrix's tactile sensitivity was so bad that she hadn't worn underwear for weeks. She couldn't bear her hair being brushed, didn't brush her teeth and refused all long sleeves.

Her mum burst into tears. She had been called into the head teacher's office because Beatrix was, according to them, looking like a neglected child, and several parents had reported her. This poor woman was beside herself. She felt so much guilt – at having left the situation to get so bad, at not being able to make herself force Beatrix to brush her hair or wear clothes, at having Beatrix go to school looking scruffy and untidy. But mostly, she berated herself because she hadn't been able to touch or hug Beatrix for over eight months. Bea's dad was fed up and the entire family was falling apart.

After my assessment, we started the Wilbarger DPPT. The first session was hard. Beatrix was scared of having me so close to her, but she accepted it. We then discussed with her that her mum would perform the technique several times a day.

Beatrix was incredibly brave and let her mum learn to do the brushing on her (after practising on me). After the extended session, they left. They were physically exhausted and emotionally drained.

I had a text message later that evening saying, 'This is so hard.'

The next day, I didn't hear from Bea's mum, and so I sent a quick message saying, 'All OK?' No reply.

The next day was Saturday. I used to run a limited clinic on Saturdays – that mummy guilt getting to me. Halfway through my last session, the doorbell buzzed. It was Beatrix and her mum and dad. I let them in while I said goodbye to the other family. I was terrified. What had happened?

When I went out to the waiting area, Bea's dad gave me a massive hug. I honestly didn't know what was happening. He was crying. Her mum was crying. Beatrix was smiling.

She had let her dad hug her for the first time in months.

This is one of those cases that will be with me forever, along with the nine-month-old baby whose mum called me late one night to tell me she had successfully changed his nappy and he hadn't cried or screamed.

Of course, this method is not right for every child. There are many other less intensive methods which work well too but take a longer time. But the payoff is amazing. Once kids feel comfortable in their skin, they are less wary and anxious, and are willing to let other people and experiences in. They no longer explode at the tiniest brush of their arm or when faced with eating 'mixed food' like a stew or casserole.

Here are some easy activities to develop the tactile system:

- Play-Doh – use cutters, rolling pins, spoons and other utensils to touch the Play-Doh until your child is more comfortable. Better yet, why not make a batch of cookies or biscuits?

- Soapy bath foam – one of my favourite items to use and recommend. It dries clear and can be easily wiped off. Clapping and stomping on the foam provides deep pressure and proprioception (see below).

- Looking for objects buried in dry beans, rice, pasta, kinetic sand, and using old serving spoons and utensils to play with them. I sing a lot so tend to incorporate songs, which can be calming.

- Finger painting with cream or custard and decorating it with sprinkles. If your child is not happy touching the cream or custard, *do not* force them. Give them a spoon or fork to stir it or a straw to blow it across their plate.

- Use a towel and rub them vigorously after a bath or shower.

- Use various brushes, loofahs and sponges in the bath.

- Massage lotion into their arms and legs. If your kids don't want you doing this, then ask them for a hand massage instead.

- Vibrating toys or massagers. Only use these if your child is not scared and give them total control of the toy. I would recommend sticking to hands, arms, legs, feet, the back and the head if your child is happy with it. Never use it on their stomach.

What is proprioception?

Proprioception is our sense of body position and movement. We gather proprioceptive information through receptors in our muscles and joints, and this lets us know where our body is in space.

Proprioceptive feedback, integrated with tactile information, is necessary for the development of a good body scheme, which enables planning and organisation of movement and 'programming' of automatic movement patterns. Good proprioception allows accurate grading of the amount of force to use for different movements. It allows me to bring a cup of tea to my mouth without looking at my hand or the cup. When kids are getting changed for PE, it allows them to do so without having to look at their clothes. Sadly, when kids have proprioceptive dysfunction, they are often wrongly labelled as clumsy, too rough or uncoordinated.

When signals between their muscles and joints aren't interpreted correctly, kids may:

- Use too much or too little pressure when writing, catching, kicking, using cutlery
- Be too rough when playing and get into trouble for pushing or bashing
- Chew their sleeves, ties, collars, pens and toys
- Fidget or jiggle their legs
- Trip and fall often
- Have difficulties walking up and down stairs
- Struggle to sit upright at the table when writing or eating
- Tire easily
- Lean on furniture or bump into things
- Slump
- Rest their heads in their hands when writing
- Struggle to stand and balance on one foot
- Have difficulties with motor planning
- Have poor postural control

How to develop the proprioceptive system

Heavy activity is something you'll hear OTs recommend all the time. And honestly, it's a godsend.

What do I mean by heavy activity? Anything that will make you use your muscles and become aware of them, even after you've stopped using them. These activities involve resistance, which gives a lot of input to our joints and muscles. As adults, we find activities to fulfil this need – lifting weights, running, gardening and digging.

Here are some simple heavy activities for kids of all ages. At home:

- Pushing or pulling laundry baskets

- Packing away canned foods

- Shaking out their duvets and blankets

- Carrying groceries into the house

- Sweeping, mopping or vacuuming the floor

- Pulling wet washing out of the washing machine and putting it into the tumble dryer

- Raking leaves

- Sweeping the patio

- Digging holes in the garden

- Kneading dough

- Trampolining
- Making an obstacle course with sofa cushions and negotiating it
- Using two-way Lycra for tug of war or swinging smaller kids

In town:

- Putting cans of food into the trolley
- Carrying shopping bags
- Having a little backpack to help carry groceries and shopping

At school:

- Taking heavy books to and from the classroom
- Cleaning the whiteboard
- Pushing chairs under tables
- Helping the dinner ladies wipe the tables
- Helping the caretaker sweep the floors

CASE STUDY – MARCO

Marco first came to see me when he was six years old and had just started Year 1. His teacher had asked his mum to bring him to see me following an INSET training

I had done for the school on identifying children with sensory processing difficulties.

Her main concerns about him included:

- Constant fidgeting and moving about on his carpet spot or in his chair
- Bumping into others
- Leaning and pushing on other kids, the teacher (especially during carpet time) and furniture
- Chewing his pencils
- Chewing his sleeves and polo shirt collar
- Unintentionally breaking crayons when drawing
- Rough playing
- Getting into trouble for pushing or hurting other children

His mum was surprised because his teacher in reception hadn't mentioned anything. She'd agreed he was rough and boisterous but put it down to having two older siblings who were always busy and active.

When we had our consultation, it dawned on his mum that the first year of school had been free-flowing: two open-plan classes of thirty kids each with dividing doors. The classrooms opened onto a big outside play area, and for most of the day, there were stations set up around them – Lego/building, drawing and crafting, dress-up and pretend play, trains and the book corner. Outside there were trikes, stilts, logs, rocking equipment, hopscotch and even a little grass-covered hill for the kids to roll down. It was basically Marco's idea of heaven.

Move to Year 1 and bam! The demands changed so drastically and quickly that many children struggled and often didn't settle down for at least a term. Marco had not changed – his environment and the learning demands had changed, and the expectations were significantly higher.

In Year 1, there is a lot more structure – after registration, there is phonics, then literacy, then handwriting practice. A quick snack time, and then more structured work. And so the day continues. In the afternoon there is a little more time for play, but not much. And this was why Marco struggled so much – he now had to sit for a lot of the day, indoors, and he had to conform to the demands of a seemingly new environment.

We only actually had to make a few changes – simple strategies that proved effective for Marco. These included him taking the registers and lunch choices to the office every morning (even though the teachers had already updated these online). Marco wore a little backpack which contained some catalogues and heavy reference books, took the register from his teacher and walked the long route to the office with another classmate. Together they collected all the registers from the other classrooms to drop off. He would give the backpack to the office staff, who exchanged his books and sent him back to class.

His mum was keen to trial some of the seating options I have in the clinic in class, and so we introduced a ball chair, two wobble cushions, a foot fidget and TheraBand on a few of the chairs, and a makeshift standing desk. We encouraged everyone to use these so that Marco didn't feel singled out.

We devised a sensory diet for Marco which incorporated a lot of heavy work – cleaning the whiteboard, carrying the fruit tray to offer to his classmates, using a weighted pencil, having a weighted lap pad for those moments when he had to sit at the table. Marco's sensory breaks all included activities such as chair push-ups, table pushes and wall pushes in class, and more movement-based ones outside the class. The teacher saw a marked improvement in Marco's engagement, and reports of him pushing other children reduced to the point of being almost non-existent.

By having these resources available to all the children in the class, the teacher soon saw the benefit the sensory input had on the whole class. She was so pleased that she had the whole class doing more proprioceptive-based 'brain breaks', which all the kids embraced. They were, in fact, arguing over the different seats, so the teacher successfully got money from the parent-teacher association and bought a few more.

The vestibular system

The vestibular system, based in the inner ear, monitors our head position and the effects of gravity. This means it allows the body to resist the force of gravity for static and dynamic balance, equilibrium reactions and anti-gravity control. The vestibular system provides an important spatial reference point for directionality, sense of body planes and organisation in space. It influences eye movements, muscle tone and bilateral integration, and helps integrate information from all the senses.

Have you noticed when you've been spinning how your eyes move rapidly from side to side? That's your vestibular system in action.

Along with your proprioceptive system, the vestibular system is fundamental to all aspects of daily life – walking upstairs, riding a bike, playing in the playground, taking a ride in the car, bending down to pick up toys, as well as simply sitting upright in a chair. As with the other senses, a child may be over-responsive to movement, for example, the kid who gets car sickness, or under-responsive – the child who is constantly running and climbing and needing to move.

CASE STUDY – JULIE

Julie wasn't one of the first pupils who sprang to teachers' minds when they thought of children who had sensory difficulties. Instead, they focused on the children who were constantly moving and fidgeting, and often hurting themselves due to their impulsivity and lack of safety awareness.

When I first saw Julie, she was standing against a wall in the playground, watching the other children play. When the bell rang for play time to end, Julie looked nervous, and then walked very slowly and cautiously. Coming to a tiny step, she hesitated for about ten seconds before awkwardly lifting one foot and putting it down on the step, followed by the other foot. She walked close to the wall as the children entered the school and was rigid and stiff when she walked into her classroom. Julie's movements were robotic and carefully calculated.

I was interested in Julie and observed her for the rest of the afternoon in the classroom. At the end of the day, I watched her become absolutely petrified when the school minibus was waiting for her to get in. The teacher said that Julie was usually upset when it was time to go home. They had even investigated whether there was any sort of abuse or unhappiness at home, but there wasn't. Julie's parents had reported that the mornings were difficult for them and she would often resist getting into the school bus, crying and clinging on to her mum.

I asked Julie's parents and teachers to fill in some sensory-based questionnaires, and when we analysed the results, it became apparent that Julie had an over-responsive vestibular system. Her parents said that they never went to the park, and she was reluctant to use escalators or lifts when they did go out.

With their consent, I started seeing Julie for some Ayres sensory integration in the school's fully-equipped room. It was a slow process and Julie was incredibly nervous when she entered the room.

Sensory integration rooms tend to have a variety of surfaces of varying heights for children to walk on, as well as a huge range of suspended equipment. It took the entire first session to get Julie to step onto the small trampoline and stand on it. It took a further three sessions before Julie would even entertain the idea of crawling onto a sturdy low-hanging platform swing.

The first time she went onto the platform swing, I had asked her mum to come in. Her mum was already sitting on it with her legs stretched out, due to it being so low, when I helped Julie shuffle backwards onto the swing and into the safety of her mum's arms (and legs). Once she was on the swing with her mum, they simply sat there for a few minutes before I asked her mum to gently move from side to side.

The movements were tiny and slow, yet Julie startled. And then she smiled.

Over the following few months, Julie made some significant progress and showed some real gains at home and at school. She was comfortable and happy to get onto the platform swing and use her feet to move herself about. She also really enjoyed lying on her tummy and using her hands to spin herself around. A major improvement was that Julie no longer cried or became distressed when she had to get on or off the school minibus.

How to develop the vestibular system:

- Jumping – on sofa cushions, trampoline, bouncy castles, on the spot, frog jumps

- Garden swings and slides

- Logrolling – on carpets, on the grass, down a hill

- Obstacle courses – over, under, through furniture and household items like sofas, chairs, beds and tables

- Combine movements with proprioception – heavy work activities

Other difficulties

The auditory system

The auditory system helps us to process sounds. We can be either over-responsive or under-responsive to noise. How we perceive sound massively affects our behaviour – we may be fine driving along with Stevie Wonder's *Superstition* playing at top volume, but as soon as we realise we are lost, we turn the volume right down to focus and concentrate.

A child who struggles with noise will have a really hard time connecting, achieving or navigating at school, or in a busy household with older brothers and sisters, two dogs, and a baby sibling. Kids who struggle with noise may:

- Overreact to household sounds such as fans, the vacuum cleaner or hairdryer

- Struggle to focus in noisy environments – they may withdraw, lash out, cover their ears, or avoid noisy environments altogether

- Hum or sing constantly to drown out sounds

- Startle easily

- Be easily upset by loud noises

Some strategies to try include:

- Proprioceptive activities

- Ear defenders

- Noise-cancelling headphones

- Mouldable silicone earplugs

- Controlling the environment – make sure you can give your child a little area on their own to do homework or read

- Positioning in class

- Avoiding noisy environments

Visual difficulties

Some children can be hypersensitive visually. They are over attuned to stimuli around them, so will struggle to screen out the bits they don't need to focus on and zoom in on what is pertinent at the time.

When children are over-sensitive to visual inputs, they may appear to be:

- Sensitive to bright lights. They often squint, cover their eyes, cry and/or complain of headaches from the light.

- Struggling to keep their eyes focused on a task they are working on for an appropriate amount of time.

- Easily distracted by the tiniest visual stimuli in the room, eg movement, decorations, windows, doorways, etc.

- Easily disorientated or irritable in brightly coloured rooms.

- Easily overwhelmed when videos are stopped and started in class as part of a lesson.

CASE STUDY – ZOEY

Twelve-year-old Zoey was attending a small independent school. She had generalised anxiety but was coping well.

About a term into the new academic year, the SENCo asked me to offer some advice. Zoey had recently started displaying significant oppositional behaviour – refusing to go into certain classes, running away and shouting. I asked the SENCo if it was all classes, and she said no, only some.

I sat in on the classes Zoey was finding particularly difficult and found the common thread: both classes were taught by incredibly enthusiastic teachers who used a range of audio-visual techniques and equipment in their lessons. They would often put videos up on the smartboard, stopping and starting them several times to make certain points.

I had asked Zoey, her parents and her form tutor to complete sensory questionnaires, and in all areas, Zoey was found to be both visually and auditorily hypersensitive.

Zoey told me, 'When the teachers stop and start a video, the noise is loud and the lights are dimmed, and the pictures on the screen are just moving images. It makes me feel so angry and nauseous that I have to get out.'

Working with Zoey, I supported her to make a personalised Sensory Ladder, which we used to build a shared narrative and understanding, allowing the teachers to provide the right support for Zoey throughout the school day. Sensory Ladders, developed by an incredibly inspirational occupational therapist Kath Smith,[17] have been used since 2001 'to support adults, teens and children with sensory integration difficulties... to create the right space, to do the right thing, to be in the right place and at the right time'.

I did some training with all the teachers so they understood the effect the stopping and starting of videos may have on some pupils. Zoey has started a listening-based therapy programme and is also allowed to leave the class when short video clips are going to be played. She watches them later, at home or in the library, at a volume and brightness level she can tolerate.

Key reminders

- Sensory processing is the way that our nervous system gets the messages from our senses and turns them into our responses or reactions.

---

17   K Smith, 'Sensory Ladders for self-regulation', www.sensoryladders. org/about

- There are actually eight senses.

- Tactile defensiveness can have a massive impact on a child and their family.

- A child can under-respond or over-respond to any sensory input, and sometimes they can even do both.

- Proprioception and vestibular inputs are like the Avengers – powerful but use them with caution (especially rotation). They're highly effective in creating organisation where there is chaos.

9
Emotional Regulation

In this chapter, you will:

- See how important emotional regulation is to respond to experiences appropriately

- Learn how to help your kids develop self-regulation

- Have a look at the different workings of the brain and how each part can affect the others

- Realise that no emotions are bad

- Discover the Zones of Regulation, devised by Leah Kuypers

Self-regulation and emotional regulation are about being able to respond to our daily experiences with emotions and actions that are not only socially accept-able, but also proportionately appropriate. Children need to learn how to monitor their emotions, moderate when they have these emotions, and then adjust how they feel their feelings and how they express them.

The ability to self-regulate is not something children are born with. Irrationality and rollercoaster swings of emotion are things toddlers excel in. And their ability to recover quickly when we, the parents, are about to lock ourselves in the bathroom at our wits' end is another wonderful skill the little nippers have.

As parents, we have to teach our children how they can self-regulate their emotions, because being able to self-regulate underpins and affects relationships and interactions (our ability to connect), functioning and success (achievement), and mental health and well-being. A child who has spectacular tantrums and is unable to self-regulate can cause a great deal of strain on the whole household – their relationship with their parents suffers, their siblings suffer, and often the parents' relationship comes under a tremendous amount of pressure. The child's inability to control their feelings and how they express them also means they find it hard to make and keep friends. Within themselves, these kids often appear anxious, angry or withdrawn.

When our kids can regulate their emotions and mod-erate their responses, they are generally better able to focus, pay attention, problem-solve, and show restraint and inhibition. Children who are able to self-regulate are equipped to cope with difficult situations and trauma and show resilience and tolerance to frustration. They are then better able to achieve success at home, in school and with their relationships, and generally have more satisfaction in life.

Helping our kids develop self-regulation and emotional moderation

Our brains have what can be thought of as three layers. First came the 'old brain' – the lizard or the reptile brain. This controls and regulates all essential functions such as our temperature, blood sugar levels and hunger and thirst. Our lizard brain is there to protect us so that we can survive. It is responsible for our 'fight, flight, fright or freeze' response.

The next layer is one only found in mammals – the midbrain, also known as the mammalian brain. This is responsible for our emotional side – fear, arousal, anxiety, sexual drive and anger reside here. This emotional state then causes the lizard brain to kick in. Our heart rate increases, and we have a stress response not for regulatory reasons, but for emotional reasons.

Our newest layer is the neocortex – this is the really smart part. Our neocortex can control our emotional state – for example, I watch *The Lion King* and get sad when Mufasa dies, so I cry. These are fictional characters, yet I feel emotional. In the same way, the neocortex affects the reptile brain, so when I think of my own mortality, I experience a brief moment where my heart rate increases.

Our brains are so awesome that the reptile brain can affect our neocortex – when I'm hungry, I am unforgiving and make harsh decisions. When I am emotional, I become impulsive and rash. It is essential to understand that while these interactions occur unconsciously, almost robotically, we can control them. By using our neocortex and simply thinking of experiences, we can, for example, control our breathing and slow down our stress response.

Here are some ways we can influence our kids' ability and support their emotional self-regulation:

Modelling

We know that our children watch everything we do, how we respond, how we express ourselves, and copy us. Think back to the first time your little one said a swear word – I remember responding with, 'Yes, duck. Did you also see the duck?' There was no duck.

And just as they copy our language, they will copy how we react. If you are prone to slamming doors, frowning, gesturing angrily and shouting, guess what? Your child will be too. When you catch yourself starting to respond in a way which doesn't serve you or your child well, try saying something like, 'That silly man is driving so badly – I feel angry,' instead of yelling while stuck in traffic.

Parenting

When we are warm, receptive, responsive and accepting, our children feel comforted, validated and relieved. We show them that we empathise with them while encouraging them to use more positive language and behaviours.

When we dismiss their feelings and responses, our children develop negative and destructive emotional regulation strategies. When I am upset and my husband tells me to calm down, I want to clobber him. When I shout at my kids for not doing their laundry and they say 'Chill, Mum', I can assure you the last thing I am feeling like doing is chilling. I know how hard it is not to react to a child's umpteenth tantrum about the colour of their sippy cup, but it is important to them (who knows why?) so we need to be patient. We need to engage our neocortex so that our lizard brain can help us slow down our stress responses.

We can create positive emotional environments by letting our children know that no emotions are bad, but there are better ways to express ourselves. I can recall getting a phone call from our new nanny saying that Xavier had locked her out of the house and wouldn't let Noah open the door for her because she wasn't paying enough attention to him.

Teaching

Until our kids are old enough to use their executive function (see Chapter 12), we must teach them how to self-regulate their emotions, using proven science-backed strategies.

Breathing – I like teaching square breathing for younger kids. I get them to trace one side of the shape while breathing in – one side while holding – two sides while breathing out. This is great because it is concrete and physical and helps them to redirect their thoughts. I also love the hand tracing breathing method.

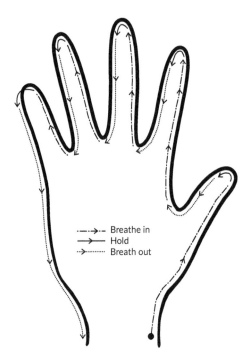

Redirect younger kids – for example, you could say, 'Oh my goodness, did you see that dog? Wow!' No? Neither did I, but now my son is looking for the dog, breathing more evenly and forgetting why he was upset in the first place.

Your child's zones

I love using the Zones of Regulation by Leah Kuypers.[18] My team and I decided we needed to get Leah over to England to present a two-day conference. This was an absolute career highlight – Leah is truly inspirational.

I always do an information session before I introduce any sort of emotional regulation programme because it is crucial that everyone understands the purpose of the programme and how to use it. Even more important is that they understand that *no emotions* are wrong or bad.

CASE STUDY – JENS

I began seeing five-year-old Jens at school after his teacher referred him for 'anger issues'. He was also struggling with his handwriting, but this was, to be frank, the least of everyone's worries. His mum was finding it difficult to connect with him and routine daily activities were a struggle.

---

18 L Kuypers, 'The Zones of Regulation: A framework designed to foster self-regulation and emotional control', www. zonesofregulation.com/learn-more-about-the-zones.html

I had recently introduced the zones to the older boys at Jens's school, and his teacher was keen for us to trial Jens with them. We started with a simple zones chart using just four colours, explaining that each colour represented different feelings. Blue was sad or tired or hurt. Green was happy, A-OK and ready to listen and learn. Yellow was worried, excited and fizzy. And red was angry, mad, cross and out of control.

Jens's mum was CEO of a Paris-based company, so she relied heavily on nannies for childcare. His dad was a journalist who was not consistently at home. In recent months, the team of nannies had changed, and Jens had struggled with this change.

He was finding dressing, bathing, swimming and mealtimes difficult. One of the nannies described him as always angry and unable to express his feelings. He would become frustrated at the smallest failure and would hit, shout, push or throw things.

I decided to introduce the same zones chart as we'd used at school into the home so it was familiar to Jens. I added small photos of all the members of the family and main household staff. As consistency and modelling were key, I held two 'training sessions'. One was for all staff and parents, where I reiterated that they needed to model their feelings. They needed to say when they were frustrated or worried.

Rollo, one of the drivers, was a calm and patient man who would naturally say things like, 'This traffic is making me mad. We may be late. Let's just listen to some music because we can't do anything about it.' Jens's mum Marie, on the other hand, would grind her teeth, bash the steering wheel, shout at the other drivers and turn different shades of red. I pointed out that no feelings are wrong, but she would be better off verbalising what she was feeling instead.

I then held a 'family meeting' – mum, dad, kids and the nannies. I explained the zones concept, which Jens was familiar with so this boosted his confidence as he could explain it to the others. We kept it simple and we kept it consistent.

Everyone started expressing themselves using words rather than actions, including the chef who was notorious for yelling. The household quickly changed. And Jens became visibly calmer over the next week. The nannies were amazing at reading his cues, and they really took everything we discussed on board.

When Marie suddenly had to take a business call one day as she and Jens were about to play a board game, Jens became very upset. He picked up the cup with the dice in and growled and looked ready to hurl it across the room. Then a little voice piped up.

'Use your zones!'

It was two-year-old Cara, holding out the zones chart. This was the longest sentence she had strung together at the time.

Jens scowled at her and said through gritted teeth, wiping tears away from his eyes, 'I'm so frustrated and cross at you, Mummy' and put the cup down.

Marie, to her credit, told everyone on the call she had to dial back in a few minutes, hung up and gave Jens a big hug.

'I know, Jens,' she said.

Key reminders

- Emotional regulation is not something we are born with.

- No emotions are bad.

- You need to model emotional regulation for your kids.

- Deep breathing is a great tool for emotional regulation.

- Tell your child how you are feeling (bearing in mind that they're not your counsellor).

10
Motor Skills

In this chapter, you will:

- Learn about the development of gross motor skills
- Understand the difference between gross and fine motor skills
- Read my top tips for developing motor skills
- Learn about the importance of bilateral coordination skills

Gross motor skills

Gross motor skills involve using all the big muscles and muscle groups in our body, such as the trunk, arms and legs. These skills usually develop from head to toe – a newborn baby learns to hold their head up first, then gets more control of the rest of their body, eventually learning to sit up, roll over, crawl and walk. The rest of the gross motor skills develop in the same way over time as the body gets stronger and the child gains better coordination.

Roughly speaking, gross motor skills develop at certain ages and stages. A baby needs to be able to pull him or herself up to standing so they can develop the muscles they need to get up and hold themselves up, so they can get ready for walking. For example:

- By about three months, a baby learns to lift their head when they are lying on their tummy.

- At six months, babies can roll over in both directions.

- By seven to nine months, a baby can often sit unaided.

- Crawling can happen anytime between seven to twelve months.

- Walking comes at between twelve and eighteen months.

- At about two years, the child can run and jump, awkwardly.

- At three years, they can climb low surfaces, stand on one foot momentarily, gallop, jump with two feet together and kick a static ball.

- By age four years, a child should be able to pedal a tricycle well.

Gross motor skills are vital for doing well at school. Kids have to be able to navigate not just through the classroom – around the furniture, sitting on the carpet, staying upright at their tables – but also in the busy playground, dining room and during PE.

A strong and stable posture provides a solid base to move on to more complex skills, such as balance, hand-eye and foot-eye coordination, reading, writing and listening. Postural muscles begin to develop from the moment we are born by the use of developmental positions during play and daily activities.

Developmental positions include tummy time, all fours (crawling), high kneeling and squatting. The muscles are continually strengthened by their everyday use when kids engage in daily activities.

Kids who are not exposed to these kinds of regular physical activities are likely to establish limited postural stability. Functionally, these kids and teenagers are inclined to have difficulty with fine motor skills such as handwriting, attention, coordination and balance.

It is so important to get kids using their muscles. Dig in the garden, get them to push furniture around and make obstacle courses at home. Encourage different positions for fine motor tasks or screens. Some examples include lying on their tummy to read or colour in, side-sitting (when a child's knees are bent and their feet are both going toward the same side of their body), long-sitting (where the legs are stretched out in front), playing on all fours – a crawling game of football, squatting, high kneeling and standing.

Fine motor skills

It is important for a child to be proficient in fine motor tasks so that they can carry out everyday tasks with dexterity, for example writing, using scissors, tying shoelaces and using cutlery.

To develop good fine motor control, a child needs:

- Hand and arm sensory awareness – tactile and proprioceptive
- Arm and hand strength
- Refined finger movements and eye-hand coordination
- To practise writing and drawing skills

Here are my top tips for developing gross and fine motor skills:

- Kids can make an all-day snack by threading Cheerios or other similar cereal onto a string to wear as a necklace or bracelet.

- Have them help prepare a picnic lunch by skewering cherry tomatoes, mozzarella balls, cheese and olives onto toothpicks or kebab sticks.

- Show kids how to roll up a pair of socks.

- Have them help hang up wet clothes/undies with pegs.

Bilateral coordination skills

Bilateral coordination refers to how well a child can use both sides of their body at the same time in a controlled way, for example, stabilising paper with one hand while writing/cutting with the other or tying up a tie. These can be tasks where both hands are doing the same motion, for example using a rolling pin to roll out some dough.

When children have difficulty with symmetrical movements, they may use only one hand when they should use two, or one leg/arm may be weaker than the other, or they may not have established a lead hand and support hand. Alternating or reciprocal movements often involve some form of rhythm, for example riding a bike or using the hands to pull themselves up using a rope. Difficulty coordinating both sides of the body can lead to significant struggles with daily living activities, such as dressing, tying shoelaces, using cutlery, making a snack, fastening a belt and putting on socks and shoes. Activities such as threading, buttoning, sewing, drawing, writing, cutting, kicking, catching, throwing, crawling, walking, going up and downstairs, as well as riding a bike or using a scooter, can be affected, leading to a range of further struggles.

The vestibular system is crucial in the development of bilateral integration skills, which is why therapists will often use specific movement patterns/activities before working on bilateral skills.

Key reminders

- Motor skills develop from gross to fine – we need to be stable closer to our midline, so that we can have greater control of our hands and feet.

- When OTs target handwriting, they often work on core strength, postural stability and shoulder stability before they actually get to putting pencils on paper.

- Bilateral integration is crucial for learning.

11
Visual Perception

In this chapter, you will:

- Learn what visual perception is, and what it is not

- Meet the key areas of visual perception

- Understand how to recognise when your child may be struggling with visual perception

- Learn some ways to help them deal with their struggles

Ever wonder why some people (like my husband and kids) cannot see a certain sock/shirt/fork even though it's really obvious to you? Visual perception is all about how our brains interpret and make sense of what our eyes see. It's *not* about our visual acuity –

someone can have perfect eyesight and still struggle with visual perception.

We need good visual perception skills so that we can read, write, cut, draw, do puzzles, work out sums, dress ourselves and find things efficiently.

The key areas of visual perception

Key areas of visual perception are:

- **Visual discrimination.** This is our ability to see subtle differences or similarities in objects, including letters and numbers, to distinguish them from others. For example, when we're sorting coins, 5p and 1p coins are similar in size, but are different colours, whereas £1 and £2 coins are similar colours, but different sizes. Our visual discrimination skills allow us to distinguish b from d, p from q, and words such as want and won't. Children who have good visual discrimination skills are able to read more fluently. Conversely, the child with weak visual discrimination is likely to struggle with or have delays in developing reading, spelling, writing and maths skills.

- **Visual form constancy.** This is our ability to know that a square remains a square whether it is red, yellow or blue, or whether it is big or small.

- **Visual closure.** This allows us to recognise a shape, word or item when we can only see part of it. It's basically how we 'fill in the blanks' and learn to read by recognising sight words – common words that we learn as a whole when we first start to read as children.

- **Visual figure-ground.** This is our ability to locate something in a busy situation, for example, find a specific pair of trainers in the shoe basket, or the fountain pen in a full pencil case.

- **Visual memory.** This is our ability to recall and remember visual specifics of a form, word, activity or object. Visual memory is absolutely essential when we're reading and writing – imagine trying to write the word 'fabulous' by copying it from the board, and you can only recall one or two letters at a time. How frustrating! Kids who struggle to write fast enough, to remember words, will often be the ones who know the answers, but can't get them down on paper quickly enough during tests.

- **Visual sequential memory.** This is really critical for reading and writing – it allows us to recall a sequence of objects, letters in a word or digits in a number in the correct order.

- **Visual-spatial relations.** These help us understand the relationships of objects within the environment. Visual-spatial relations have laterality – knowing left and right on ourselves –

and directionality – being able to know right and left on other objects – at their core.

Recognising struggles with visual perception

Children who struggle with their visual perception may show difficulties:

- Doing puzzles
- Completing dot-to-dot pictures
- Knowing what you mean when you say in, out, on, under, next to, up, down, in front of
- Differentiating b from d, p from q
- Writing numbers or letters the right way round
- Keeping their place when reading or writing
- Knowing their left from their right
- Remembering the order of the letters of the alphabet
- Copying – from a book or whiteboard
- Matching – socks, shoes, shapes
- Distinguishing the size of letters and objects
- Remembering basic sight words

- Sorting and organising personal belongings – they may have a messy desk or bedroom

At home and school, you can help them by providing:

- Square/graph paper to aid word spacing and sizing, and maths.

- Paper with differentiated lines.

- Paper copies. It is much easier for kids to copy from a sheet next to them than to have to look up at the board.

- Alphabet strip. Place one of these on your child's desk for them to refer to for correct letter formation.

- Dot-to-dot games.

- Construction-type activities such as Duplo, Lego or other building blocks like Meccano, Zoobs and Stickle Bricks are excellent toys.

You can also:

- Encourage your child to keep their desk clear of distractions and clutter.

- Position their desk away from distractions. Liaise with their teacher about putting their desk near the front.

- Eliminate visual distractions. Keep your fridge and their room walls clear of posters and pictures.

- Use a red marker to outline the boundaries to help them with cutting.

- Use hidden-picture games in books such as *Where's Wally?* or *Spot the Difference.*

- Encourage your child to be the teacher and mark your work. Give them a red pen and some stickers – kids love being the teacher.

OTs usually screen a child's visual perceptual skills, and then decide if an in-depth assessment is needed.

Key reminders

- Visual perception has a huge role to play in your child's performance and achievement at school.

- Visual perception is not visual acuity – your child can have perfect eyesight, and still struggle with visual perception.

- There are many ways to recognise if your child is struggling with visual perception, and to help them to deal with these struggles.

12
Executive Function

In this chapter, you will:

- Discover what executive function means

- Understand the difficulties faced by children who struggle with executive function

- Learn how to support your child's executive function

- See how executive function and ADHD are related

- Read how I was diagnosed with ADHD at the age of forty-two

- Look at whether to medicate your child

- Understand the medication that works for one child won't necessarily work for another

Executive function is a group of mental skills which allow us to connect what we have experienced previously with our current and present actions. When we make plans, organise, prepare, pay attention, and follow directions and instructions at home, school or work, or on the playground, we are using our executive function skills. Of the five foundational skills we are covering in this section, executive function is the one that is most often overlooked, but it is just as important as the others.

Executive function includes how well we inhibit ourselves, shift our thoughts, control our emotions, initiate tasks, remember tasks, plan and organise events, organise materials and self-monitor. Children who have problems with their executive functions will invariably struggle with:

- Keeping track of time
- Making plans
- Starting and finishing activities
- Organising their homework
- Planning a group project
- Getting ready for school
- Prioritising tasks
- Following directions

- Controlling their emotions and behaviour (they can often be quite annoying)

- Coping with changes in routines

- Looking after their belongings

- General time management

How to support your child's executive function

You can support your child's executive function by teaching *and modelling* strategies such as:

- Using checklists effectively – not just making a list, but actually following it.

- Packing their bags the night before they need them. Use their school timetable to see what they need and don't need. This avoids them lugging unnecessarily heavy bags.

- Using timers on phones/watches or tablets to keep them on track.

- Breaking big assignments into chunks.

- Writing the date at the top of each page or assignment.

- Organising their work into folders for different subjects.

- Making visual charts of routines or chores which they can easily follow to stay on track.

- Tidying-up after themselves. A sandwich is only made and ready to eat once they have cleared up.

Difficulties in any of the foundational skills can cause children to experience a real struggle with connection and can affect individuals in different ways. Executive function difficulties often look like the signs of ADHD because ADHD is a problem with executive function.[19]

MY EXPERIENCE

When I was growing up, I was an eccentric yet lovable child. I can remember trying a range of activities and always doing something or other, and I was the child who had five or more hobbies and projects on the go at any one time.

As I got older, I began to struggle with friendships. I found it difficult to be part of a group project at school and often struggled to control my emotions and behaviour. I would say things which were mean or hurtful, or simply inappropriate.

Up until a few months ago, I was incredibly impulsive – I routinely bought things online (several times a day), was easily distracted, made careless mistakes, lost or misplaced items and found myself unable to stick to tasks which I found tedious or boring. I was constantly

---

19 'Attention deficit hyperactivity disorder', NHS, www.nhs.uk/conditions/attention-deficit-hyperactivity-disorder-adhd/symptoms

flitting from one activity to the next, often changing the topics of conversations and leaving those I was speaking to completely confused. I can recall saying to a friend that my brain was always on the go.

She looked at me and said, 'That's simply the way you're wired.' When I said the same to Zayn, he would reply that's just the way I am.

'It's your brilliant mind,' he'd say. And I believed it. After all, I run a successful business, am in a loving marriage, have two great teenagers, a loyal dog and beautiful friends. On the outside, I appeared to have the perfect life, albeit enhanced by a high dose of fluoxetine to manage my anxiety and depression. But following a big and somewhat traumatic turnover of staff, and having new people join my team, I suddenly felt more anxious. I was drinking more gin than was good for me, and so I stopped drinking altogether, but this only exacerbated my feelings of being distracted and anxious. I felt as though I was constantly having to repeat myself, hurrying people along, saying things and regretting it, being impulsive, struggling to focus, and having difficulties organising and planning my time for reports, appraisals and general admin.

After diagnosing myself on Google (as you do), I made an appointment to see a private psychiatrist. I was convinced that I had high-functioning autism/ Asperger's and was keen to know more. I completed questionnaires (having the tables turned on me, I was now the one getting ready to be assessed), Zayn and the kids completed some too, and off I went to Harley Street. After chatting to the psychiatrist for about thirty minutes, I sat back, exhausted and eagerly awaiting my diagnosis.

As he was giving me feedback, I can clearly remember saying to him, 'Are you deliberately speaking slowly?' and he smiled.

'Well, you certainly do not have autism. You do, however, meet all the criteria for ADHD – moderate to severe, in my opinion.'

He explained that anxiety and depression are common in people who have ADHD, and that my symptoms most likely seemed worse to me when I stopped my recreational drug use (alcohol is a drug, the only one we do not have to explain using) and self-medication. I laughed and argued that I was the least hyperactive person I knew. He then asked if I'd never noticed how I jiggle my legs, fidget constantly, sit on the edge of the chair, check my phone and become easily distracted by everything.

'It's not all bad,' he said. 'Look, your blood pressure is nice and low, and your impulsivity has meant that you've always jumped in and taken risks. You're spontaneous and creative. I bet you're an amazing OT!' No wonder, I realised then, I'd always fully immersed myself in therapy sessions and ended up as exhausted as some of the kids.

Yes – I was diagnosed with ADHD at the age of forty-two. The medication has literally changed almost all aspects of my life – my relationships, my decision making, my friendships, my anxiety and my sleep. I'm still creative, funny, spontaneous and generous, but I now fully engage in a conversation.

My husband told me recently that before my diagnosis, he couldn't remember the last time we'd sat down and had a conversation without me watching TV, or checking my phone, or typing on my laptop. And he couldn't remember the last time we talked about just one thing and I'd stayed on topic.

To medicate or not to medicate?

Only you can make that decision. Using medication is not a failure – for a long time, my husband refused to give Xavier melatonin, but after several discussions with the sleep professor, he agreed to try it. After the professor tweaked the dose, Xavier finally got some sleep, which meant he was more connected at home and school, achieving more and generally much happier in himself.

I thought that because melatonin worked for Xavier, it would work for Noah. But it didn't. I learned the hard way that what works for one child in a family won't necessarily work for another.

Every child, every family, every situation is different, so do your research and get your facts from reputable sources. If you do decide to try medication, then commit to it and give it time to kick in. At the same time, don't hesitate to stop or try something else if the side-effects are too great.

Key reminders

- Sensory processing, emotional regulation, motor skills, visual perception and executive function are the foundational skills OTs work on to develop independence and skills in a child's daily occupations, but in general, executive functioning is overlooked.

- The symptoms of struggles with executive functioning are similar to, and related to, those of ADHD.

- Using or not using medication is a personal choice, but what works for one child may not work for their sibling. Do your research. Give the medication time, but if it's not working for your child, stop it or try something else.

PART FOUR
NAVIGATE

13
Independence

In this chapter, you will:

- Guide your conundrum child through the key stages in their life now you have recognised what they can achieve

- Appreciate the importance of independence

- Redefine chores as contributions in your home

- Examine whether kids should be paid for the contributions they make

- Understand the contributions children should be making at certain ages

- Find out what motivates your child to contribute

- Learn how to use the word 'yes' to benefit both you and your child

The *Cambridge English Dictionary* defines navigate as 'to direct the way that a ship, aircraft, etc will travel, or to find a direction across, along, or over an area of water or land, often by using a map.'[20]

The *Oxford Learner's Dictionary* defines navigate as '[transitive]: navigate something – to find the right way to deal with a difficult or complicated situation.'[21]

Once you accept what your conundrum child can do, you'll know what they can achieve, and that means you can guide them to navigate their way through all the key stages of life and help them become independent.

CASE STUDY – BRIC

I was sitting in a review meeting with teachers and parents – the teachers and the child's mum had specifically requested I attend, because the dad was having a hard time accepting Bric's difficulties. I had explained that it was the dad's journey and we needed to be patient.

We started the meeting, and the teacher and SENCo went through Bric's strengths. His teacher said

---

20 Cambridge English Dictionary, www.dictionary.cambridge.org/dictionary/english/navigate

21 Oxford Learner's Dictionary, www.oxfordlearnersdictionaries.com/definition/english/navigate

something like, 'His maths is a strength – he knows number bonds to ten...'

Before she could finish her sentence, Bric's dad said, 'So his maths is a strength, and he is barely mediocre at that.' I can't remember the exact phrase he used, because in that moment, while everyone else gasped, I only recall feeling so sad.

Until that dad accepts Bric for just how awesome and unique he is, he won't understand how much Bric can actually achieve and that he can be successful, independent and contribute to his community.

To contribute to their community, your child needs certain skills. Once they have those, you can help them put them together to navigate through the different stages and phases of their life.

Building independence

As an OT, a mum and a business owner, I have independence at the forefront of my mind. Everyone, regardless of their abilities, can achieve independence in some way, and through that achieve success in at least some areas of their lives, which will promote contribution to their community.

We prepare our kids for independence as we go along. We take them to swimming lessons so that they can survive if they fall into a swimming pool. We don't teach them to swim so that we can go on lovely summer holidays. Ultimately, we want our kids to be independent. I would love for my kids to do whatever they love doing and earn enough money to move out of my house – ideally before they are thirty-five years old.

Developing and building independence is really about growing a child's skills. It fosters self-reliance and allows them to feel like they have some control over their lives.

When our kids are younger and we constantly say no to them, they are likely to react by being resistant and angry. Think of those little toddler tantrums – you say no, and they explode. What this often leads to is kids becoming indifferent about tasks at home, so when you ask them to do something, say unload the dishwasher, their response is no.

It is important to give children the skills to be independent because it leads to them becoming autonomous and self-sufficient. The confidence they get from saying 'I can do it on my own' or 'Look – I did it by myself' gives them a sense of self-efficacy which boosts self-esteem, motivation and perseverance in school and in life.

It is amazing to watch young children at nursery or in the early years of school. They are so keen to help when they are able to do something others can't – 'I helped Todd with his coat today and showed him how to hang it on his peg.' And this leads to self-esteem and confidence and a feeling of pride.

MY EXPERIENCE

I remember one of the first sleepovers Xavier had (at our house, of course). In the morning, the boys woke up and wanted fried eggs and crispy bacon for breakfast. I told Xavier to make it himself, something he had wanted to learn because he didn't like the way we did the eggs, and so we had taught him how to do it safely, and how to do it well. This skill benefited us hugely when he would make us a hangover breakfast.

And on this morning, he got everything together the boys needed to make their breakfast. His friend Miles was stunned; he couldn't believe that we allowed this – that Xavier could use the cooker and crack an egg correctly, and that he was doing it so well. He told us that his parents never let him near the cooker, and he had never thought of doing it for himself.

Xavier asked him if he wanted to have a go at flipping his egg and proceeded to show Miles how to do it. He then gave the turner to Miles and stood back. When Miles struggled and yolk came oozing out, he immediately said how rubbish he was, and tried to hand over the tools to Xavier, who refused and told Miles to practise with the other eggs. Miles, of course, smashed it (not literally) and asked me to take photos to send to his parents. He was so proud of himself and his confidence went through the roof.

By teaching our kids independence, we also teach them about failure, making mistakes and working under pressure and stress. We have opportunities to help them confront negative feelings in a somewhat controlled situation and guide them in how to deal with not necessarily achieving what they set out to do.

Being independent means our children learn to make decisions, solve problems, make plans based on their previous successes and failures, take on responsibilities, help others, teach others and be more confident. We can and must use all opportunities to allow our kids to be more independent. And at home, this can start with so-called chores.

Contributions, not chores

I was watching some kids in the clinic waiting room one day and observed how they handed their rubbish to their mum to put in the bin, gave their shoes and coat to her, and expected to be dressed. What was interesting was that this behaviour generally seemed to come from the neurotypical siblings. The parents had consciously worked on their non-neurotypical child's independence skills because they were aware that these skills needed to be developed and refined, so here we had our little conundrum child opening their own raisins, putting the empty box in the bin, putting on their shoes and coat, while Mum helped their neurotypical siblings to do the same things.

It dawned on me that while I had worked hard on developing what I perceived to be basic skills in Xavier, I had not done so for Noah. As a result, Xavier was far more independent at an early age than Noah, eager to contribute to daily tasks, while Noah was not so much.

The word 'chore' is generally associated with something unpleasant and boring which needs to be done routinely and regularly. I used to make quite a big deal of everyone doing 'their share', 'their bit to help', and assigning chores. Only recently did I change my thinking and realise that the things we do on a daily basis are *not* chores; they are how we contribute to our community. Initially, this is our home, so household chores are really household contributions. We assign our kids 'jobs', but what they are in fact doing is making a worthwhile contribution. Contributions then extend to nursery and pre-school. And so this continues in all areas of their lives.

Should kids be paid for contributions?

No, I don't pay my kids for getting themselves dressed, or putting their shoes on, or carrying their backpacks. And yet they are contributing to their community – generally speaking, they're making my life a little bit easier. The reward is in the outcome – if you clean your room, it won't smell; when you do your own laundry, it doesn't get mixed up with anyone else's; when you cook a nice meal, you eat food that you enjoy and find comforting. If my boys don't like what I am cooking, for example, I've made sure they have the skills to make a sandwich.

Do I pay my kids for jobs? Yes, I do. But I call them projects.

For example, last summer my boys had the project of scanning all my husband's and my old accounts. This was a paid job because they had to manage their time and fit it in alongside their daily household contributions, schoolwork and socialising.

Contributions by age

At ages two and three, children can:

- Tidy up toys and books.
- Pull their blankets over their cot/toddler bed.
- Help with laundry. Putting clothes into the washing machine and taking wet clothes out are great proprioceptive inputs.
- Help feed pets.
- Help wipe up the table after meals.

At ages four and five, children can:

- Load and unload plastic items in the dishwasher. If you're a bit controlling about the way your dishwasher is packed, then give them a picture of how you like it done. This will help develop their visual perceptual skills, too.

- Wash plastic dishes in the sink. Put a thermometer on the taps in case they decide to add more water – a lovely tactile activity.

- Use a hand-held vacuum cleaner for crumbs – good for strength and proprioceptive input.

- Unpack fruit and vegetables after grocery shopping.

- Water plants – indoors and outdoors.

At ages six to eight, children can:

- Make their own bed – great for proprioceptive input and shoulder strength.

- Vacuum and sweep their own room – proprioceptive input and shoulder strength.

- Prepare simple meals – breakfast, sandwiches and spreads on toast.

- Fold and put away their own laundry – fine motor skills, visual perception.

- Peel vegetables using safe peelers (you can even get left-handed peelers).

- Wipe the sink after brushing their teeth (I know this is an extra contribution on top of a contribution, but it's too important to leave out).

At ages nine to twelve, children can (top 10):

- Make a cup of tea or coffee.
- Do the online grocery shop.
- Unpack all the groceries.
- Do their own laundry. My boys learned to use the washing machine at the age of nine or ten purely accidentally as I was busy with dinner and they needed clean rugby kit, so they did it while I gave instructions.
- Prep and cook simple meals – boil an egg, make a toasted sandwich, fry bacon.
- Sew a button or hem.
- Iron a t-shirt or school shirt.
- Walk the dog (start with short walks).
- Mow the lawn.
- Change and launder their own bedding (my boys had a thing about each other's germs, so I said if they didn't want me doing their washing together, they could do their own).

At ages thirteen to eighteen, teenagers can:

- Replace lightbulbs and batteries.
- Take the rubbish out.

- Do their own laundry every week, including washing, drying, folding and ironing.

- Prepare the grocery list, go to the shop and buy items they need.

- Manage their money using a parent-linked bank account.

Motivation

Why should our kids do chores…? I mean, contribute? Why would they want to? What is in it for them?

I often get asked why children won't do what their parents ask them to do. I hear:

- He never does what I tell him to

- She doesn't do what I want her to do when I want her to do it

- He's not interested in doing anything around here

I often respond the same way: 'What is in it for them? Why should they do it?' And parents generally answer, 'Because I told them to' or 'When I was young, we did everything we were told or asked to do'.

And why do you think we did everything we were asked to do? In my household, it was because we were well aware that if we said no, we would get a smack. If we didn't do it, we would get a smack. If we did it badly – yes, smack again. That was our motivation. We didn't do as we were asked because it made us feel all warm and fuzzy inside; we were scared of the consequences.

I have listened to parents have this discussion so often. They argue about/discuss their children not wanting to do anything, blaming each other for spoiling their kids and making them entitled. Often, they say that the kids used to be helpful and happy to do tasks when they were younger and keen to be independent, but no longer.

CASE STUDY – STEPHEN

During a family feedback session, I remember both parents were very grumpy and irate. They told me that the day before, they had been at work and come home to find the house untidy, the recycling bins overflowing, and yet none of their children had done anything about this. The kids were home on school holidays with seemingly nothing better to do.

Mary, the mum, explained, 'I found myself getting more and more irate every time I saw these things that no one had done anything about. When the explosion finally came, I said to them, "You guys do nothing around here. Dad and I work our butts off, and you just treat us like servants. Why should we do anything for you if you won't help around the house?"'

Stephen, the couple's intelligent fourteen-year-old, looked at me and shrugged. 'They never asked us to do it. It doesn't bother anyone else but them. We hate doing those things, it's gross.' And his list of reasons continued.

Mary retorted with, 'I have been going around the house mentioning all the stuff that needs doing, yet no one has taken the hint.'

Stephen's response? 'You were basically talking to yourself. You didn't directly ask us to do something. You have to be direct and tell us, be specific. Hinting means nothing to us. And tell us why we need to do it.'

These kids were not motivated – they had no desire to do something which essentially wasn't important to them. They weren't getting anything out of it and had no enthusiasm for it. Once we had established this, we could then have a discussion about what was in it for the kids.

As adults, we work to earn money. We clean the kitchen floor so we can walk on it barefoot, knowing we won't be getting who-knows-what stuck to our feet. We do the washing so we have clean clothes.

Give your kids a reason to contribute to the household – that is their motivation. The reason may be 'I am so tired and would really appreciate you unloading the dishwasher before I start supper, because it will make my life easier. And it will mean supper can be ready sooner because I won't have to spend time doing that.' The fact that they can eat sooner is often a massive motivating factor for hungry kids.

Think about the motivation – some would call it the consequence. Why would your kids want to do anything? And be clear, be specific. For example, 'If you tidy your toys, then we can get a board game out, but if you don't, we'll have nowhere to sit and pieces will go missing. So, if you want to play the board game (their motivation), then tidy the floor (your expectation).' Of course, there will be push-back, but I have found that when you set the expectation and explain the consequences of not meeting it – 'If you don't tidy up, we won't have time to play the game before dinner' – your kids will be more likely to get on with their contribution.

With our conundrum kids in particular, we cannot assume that they know why something is important or helpful to us. We need to explain it to them using their own experiences and discuss it through. Tell them that you appreciate what they're doing.

'I really appreciate you doing that because it means I can have a cup of tea.'

This is so important for our conundrum kids – they don't get the social nuances. They may not see us being stressed as anything they can influence.

MY EXPERIENCE

Noah is more likely than Xavier to make me a cup of tea, often without me asking, when I am stressed. Xavier needs to be told why I want a cup of tea and how it will help my stress levels. He may not always 'get it', but when I explain this, he sees the logic behind it.

He is then likely to say to himself, 'Mum is busy and wants a cup of tea (my expectation), but she doesn't have time to make one, and Noah isn't here right now to do it (his usual excuse), so I will be helping her by doing it. Then she'll probably be quicker with making supper (his motivation).'

Motivation is so important when we set goals for our kids, which ultimately will lead them to independence. As parents, we have goals we want our kids to achieve, and yet we often don't ask them what it is that they want, what is important to them, what would make them happy or proud.

Navigating saying yes

As a parent, I find myself being asked hundreds of questions. Xavier in particular quizzes me all the time, but I've realised he is not trying to be annoying; he genuinely wants an answer.

Closed questions – when the asker wants a simple yes or no – are much easier to answer than open-ended questions. Basically, the asker wants you to say yes, but I went through a stage with the boys where every second word out of my mouth seemed to be no:

- No – you can't eat only one carrot

- No – you can't sit on your brother's head

- No – you can't not do your homework

- No – you can't go to bed without a shower or bath

- No – you can't get the paints out

- No – you can't go hang out in town

- No – you can't not go on the school trip

I've realised that when I say no, they say no, so if I ask them to do something and they say no, it's because they are following my example. By being flexible, creative and relaxed (or, as one of the boys once said, sneaky), I can say yes, giving them the feeling they're trustworthy and validated.

Three ways you can say yes:

- Yes, if… teaches your child independence and lets them learn that their choices and their actions have consequences, which they must be responsible for.

- Yes, when… gives them responsibility, trust and the idea that they generally have to wait for good things. And there is often a condition attached to them.

- Yes, and… lets them think about more than just themselves and include others.

Here are some examples:

Can I have a biscuit? Yes, if you eat your dinner. Yes, when you've tidied your books.

Can I get this toy? Yes, when it's your birthday. Yes, and let's get one for your sister, too.

Can I leave my homework? Yes, if it is not due tomorrow. Yes, when you've written a letter to your teacher explaining why you didn't do it.

Can Miles come for a sleepover? Yes, when your project is done. Yes, if you take out the recycling.

Can I go hang out in town? Yes, if you turn your 'track-my-phone' app on. Yes, and get some milk from the shop on your way back, please.

Can I use the car to go to Fred's house? Yes, and you can drop Sally off at her friend's house on the way. Yes, if you put some petrol in.

Can I go to Sienna's house party? Yes, if you give me the number for her parents. Yes, when you've finished cleaning your room.

Obviously, you're not going to say yes to everything, but be flexible. Do not shy away from saying 'Let me think about it' or 'I need to chat to your mum/dad before I can answer you'. And sometimes, no is no.

Key reminders

- Independence builds success, confidence and self-esteem.

- Making sure your kids contribute to their environment and community in a positive manner is a great way to build independence.

- When you plan who contributes what at home, ask your kids to choose what they want to do.

- Explain that they can't always do what they want – there are consequences to them not contributing. These consequences will become their motivation to do as you ask.

- Explain how and why them contributing at home is important to you.

- Tell your kids you appreciate them and their contributions.

- There's motivational power in the word yes… with conditions.

14
Ready, Steady, Go!

In this chapter, you will:

- Write a curriculum vitae (CV) for the stages of your child's life

- Prepare your child for a playdate so it won't be daunting for them

- Prepare other people to respond to your child

- Prepare your child for secondary school

- Prepare your child for when things go wrong

Imagine you had to write a CV for your child at the different stages of their life. What would be the key skills for them to enter the next phase? For example, what qualities would a childminder be looking for in your toddler? What about the skills your pre-school child needs to settle well into reception?

During the summer holidays, my practice runs a group called Ready, Steady, School! Many kids enter reception and are lost in terms of what we may consider to be essential skills – getting changed for PE, opening their snack boxes, listening, sitting in a circle, etc. This group runs over the course of a week and kids who are about to enter reception in September come in for two hours every day. They bring their snacks and their PE kit, and we run through the expectations of school while developing gross and fine motor skills in a practical way – balancing on one leg while getting changed or having enough hand and finger strength to unclip and re-clip their snack boxes. These are skills and qualities that would look great on your child's CV when they go into the next stage in their career as a great kid.

Your child's CV

Ready, steady, let's go to nursery

Goals – I will be able to:

- Be kind
- Use the toilet by myself
- Follow instructions

- Copy action songs

Independence skills – I can:

- Use a spoon and a fork
- Look at books on my own
- Build with blocks
- Listen to a story

Emotional health – I:

- Share with others
- Spend a few hours away from home
- Tell an adult if I am upset or sad

Communication – I'm learning to:

- Play with my friends
- Follow rules
- Use words to describe when I'm unhappy

I do my best to:

- Walk up and down the stairs holding onto a rail
- Run with my friends
- Get up and down from the floor and a chair easily

Ready, steady, let's go to big school

Share this with your child's teacher when they come for the home visit just before your child enters reception

Goals – I will be able to:

- Line up
- Follow a routine
- Sit on a carpet
- Listen to a story

Independence skills – I can:

- Take my coat off
- Hang my coat up
- Open and close my snack box
- Recognise my name
- Put my shoes on

Emotional health – I:

- Share with others
- Help others
- Tell an adult if I am upset or sad

Communication – I'm learning to:

- Play with my friends
- Follow rules
- Use words to express when I'm unhappy
- Wait my turn and not shout out

I do my best to:

- Change myself for games and PE without falling over too much
- Keep up when I run and play
- Carry my tray at lunchtime
- Walk around the class without bumping into others
- Try new activities, even when I'm unsure of them

Ready, steady, let's go on a playdate

Going to play at the home of a school friend can be daunting and even traumatic for some children. They understand the rules and expectations at school and in their own homes, but when they are invited to play at another child's house, they are in uncharted territory. Usually the parents who have older kids are the first ones to invite new friends for a playdate as their kids tend to be a lot more confident and at ease with the idea than only children.

Goals – I will be able to:

- Share my friends' toys
- Play with my friends' siblings
- Listen to an adult who is not my parent or teacher
- Follow the rules of another home

Independence skills – I can:

- Take my coat off
- Take my shoes off and put them back on
- Go to the toilet and wash my hands
- Use my cutlery

Emotional health – I:

- Share with others
- Help others
- Tell an adult if I am upset or sad

Communication – I'm learning to:

- Play with children I don't know
- Follow new rules
- Use words to express when I'm unhappy

Prepare for a playdate

If your child has never been on a playdate without you, prepare them fully. It is so important that the first playdate without you goes well, as it will give them the confidence for future playdates. This is what I would suggest you do:

Tell the other parent(s) about your child: Tell them everything they may need to know that will help your child feel happy, less anxious, and safe. Many parents have said to me that other mums and dads must think they are completely neurotic when they tell them about their kids, and I say, 'So what? You are a responsible parent letting them know what may or may not happen.'

I have honestly had so many kids come for playdates who don't know how to wipe their bottoms, or only eat crunchy beige food, or are vegetarian. I have no problems whatsoever wiping bottoms or not serving fish fingers; I just want to know. My one caveat would be not to share these details about your child with parents in front of your *or* their child – especially if it is something like not being able to wipe their bottom.

Clarify who your child will be travelling home with: Make sure that you have told the teacher and the school office who your child is going home with and remind your child who they are going home with, too.

If at all possible, find the parent in question the morning of the playdate and say, 'Look, it's Todd's mum. Remember you're going home with them today for awesome play.' If your child finds separating from you tricky, then it's only fair that you pick them up with the other parent and drop them at their friend's house.

Prepare your child: If their friend has siblings or pets, tell your child about them in advance. And if their friend practises a different religion to yours, or has two mums or two dads, make sure your child knows about this, too, especially if this is a new experience for them.

Be on time: When you're picking your child up from their friend's house after the playdate, arrive when you say you will – not just for your child's sake, but also for the other parent who is most likely keen to get on with their evening routine. Plan for the pick-up to take longer than you expect and read your child's cues. If they look tired or worried or grumpy, now is not the time to insist on them being independent. You want to avoid any potential outbursts.

Finally, don't reciprocate by inviting the friend for a playdate at your house until you've had a debrief with your child. They may not have got along with their friend and potentially don't want this friend at their house.

Starting secondary school

How can you not think of your little four-year-old starting school when you are preparing them (and you) for secondary school? Successfully starting a new school is all about confidence – which comes from independence. I know I am constantly saying it, but independence is key.

Your child's primary school will have done a huge amount to prepare all the kids for senior school, like assigning responsibilities such as being monitors or serving on the school council. Your child will likely have been at just one primary school, and by the time Year 6 comes around, they are quite comfortable and confident in what is expected of them. They know everything and everyone and find the little ones who visit the school 'so cute'.

You need to prepare them to go back to being that cute little kid, starting their big new school. They will know next to nothing about it – if they're lucky, they will know some kids from their primary school, but they need to be prepared for the size of secondary schools. These schools tend to be so huge that they are unlikely to be in the same class or sets as their friends.

The first thing I would suggest you do is have an informal chat with the secondary school SENCo – if you feel your child is particularly vulnerable in certain situations, then let them know. They can then identify a key person for your child to check in with. Even just knowing this adult by name and recognising their face will help set your child, and everyone else, at ease.

Don't be tempted to bombard your kids with questions after school – they will be exhausted. Play it cool – don't show them how needy you are in wanting to know every detail of every minute. (Maybe that's just me?)

Here are some practical tips to improve your child's confidence about starting secondary school:

Attend all open-day events: Familiarise yourself with the school website – it will usually contain pretty much everything you need to know, including the week and term calendars, the lunch menu, policies, who to contact, what to wear and the code of conduct. My son (who loves rules) studied the student handbook in detail and knew everything – in theory – before he started. It helped him feel more confident.

Uniform: Find out exactly what your child can and can't wear. If they are tactile sensitive, get the uniform early enough to wash it a few times and allow them to get used to how it feels.

Put in plenty of practice at tying a school tie. Your child will need to be able to do it quickly as they will often be in a hurry, for example after PE. Find out if they will need to do it in different styles and practise them all. Once they can do this with their eyes shut, then – and only then – practise putting it on and taking it off without undoing it.

If your child has to wear a blazer for the first time, resist the temptation to buy a big size for them to grow into. Kids need to use their hands. You can always sell it at the second-hand uniform shop.

For some children, it is important to wear what everyone else is wearing, eg skirts vs trousers, short sleeves vs long sleeves, jumper or not. Go and visit the school just before the summer holidays to see what the other kids are wearing. But most importantly, make sure your child is comfortable.

Travel: How will your child get to school? If you won't be driving them, make sure you familiarise them with all aspects of their travel – their route, the bus timetable, who they will walk with, how long it will take. Do they need a bus pass? Does this need a photo on it? Do you need to top it up or does this happen automatically? And practise taking the journey with them a few times.

If you're going to be driving them, practise the journey, too. Know where to drop them off and pick them up. And plan for things to go wrong. Hide some cash in their inside blazer pocket for emergencies. Make sure they have memorised both parents' phone numbers and carry a small fully-charged portable charger and cable for their phone.

Timing and organisation: As soon as your child is ready, but no later than Year 6, buy them an alarm clock. Secondary schools start early, so your child will have to get up earlier, eat breakfast earlier and be a functioning human being earlier than they have been used to. Make sure they practise – work on their time management.

I do lots of time-guessing activities with older kids – guess how long it will take you to walk to the school office and back to class. Guess how long it will take you to do five English questions. Being able to estimate time is important.

When your child gets their timetable, make multiple copies – it *will* get lost. Keep one in their bag, blazer, locker, and a few at home. Help your child use their timetable to pack their bag and prepare for the next day the night before. There is nothing more stressful than running around at 7.55am looking for PE shorts or 'the other maths book' when you're due to leave at 8am.

Find out how the locker works. If it uses a combination lock, have your child practise how to open it. If it's a keyed lock, make sure they have spare keys.

Breaks and lunches: Sometimes, secondary school lunchtime is at 11.30am. My boys were shocked by this and ended up starving by the end of the day. Find out when they will eat lunch and how long they will have. Work out how they will pay for lunch – if possible, pay a term in advance. You may have to negotiate a budget.

Prepare your child for the fact that they may have to queue for their lunch – and that older, bigger pupils push in. If they are sensitive to others touching them, it is much easier for them to deal with this and prepare mentally if they know it's a possibility.

Make sure they know that playtime is now called 'break' and often kids just 'hang out'. Tell your child where to find the library – it is a little haven for kids who want to relax, avoid the noise or do some homework at break.

When things go wrong

I am a worrier. I think about everything that could go wrong, and then I panic and catastrophise. This in turn leads to me being quite stressed when the boys try new activities or do things for themselves.

Things *will* go wrong. Otherwise, life would be boring, right? We need to prepare our kids for when things do go wrong.

Some things which have been useful to me and other families I work with:

- Your child must absolutely learn both parents' telephone numbers off by heart

- Give them a bank card linked to yours for emergencies

- Teach them how to get cash out of the ATM when they have lost their card

- Make sure they carry a small portable phone charger – which is charged

- Keep emergency cash (£10) hidden with your child's travel card or in their phone case

- Play board games – teach your kids how to lose (and win) graciously

- Ask for help

CASE STUDY – ELI

Eli is a delightful six-year-old. He is fun, charming and engaging when he gets his way and when others do what he tells them to do.

Eli absolutely adores board games, and each week he brings one into our session as his class has a bring-a-game day on the same day. His mum tells me what he's bringing in so I can plan to use it in our session and practise. We want, and need, Eli to lose sometimes, or only win by a narrow margin.

When Eli wins, he is happy. He won't quite rub it in my face, but he comes close, so we started working on turn-taking and losing.

Eli also loves dancing and is obsessed with the TV show Strictly Come Dancing. He often comes in, does a dance routine, and asks me and his learning support assistant to give him a score. In true Eli form, he argues with 'the judges' if his score is anything below a seven.

One day, Eli asked me if he was the best dancer I knew, and I said, 'No, I think I am better.' And so started the dance-offs. Initially, Eli won (his learning support assistant was the judge), but gradually, our scores started getting close until it was a draw.

Eli was not happy. We agreed that we would practise and there would be a proper three-judge dance-off the following week.

On the day, the boy I saw before Eli was late leaving, so I asked him and his teaching assistant to stay and judge. I am not embarrassed to say I went full-on Jane Fonda meets Dirty Dancing meets J-Lo and brought my A-game, going through an elaborate warm-up routine.

Eli chose the song and went first. He was good, but I was better, although I do still feel sorry for the teenager who had to sit through my stomping about like a wild elephant.

Then came the scores: Eli was awarded a seven, an eight and an eight point five. We waited with bated breath for my scores – seven, eight, and... nine (I had already subtly hinted to the other boy to give me a higher score than he had given Eli).

I did a ridiculous victory dance, and then stopped myself and said, 'Sorry for being a bad winner.'

And Eli, bless his heart, came up to me, looking lip-tremblingly sad, extended his hand and said, 'Good job, Mrs Bore (Eli cannot say the letter l), well done.' He then packed up his bags, turned and said, 'What song shall we dance to next week, Mrs Bore?' And so he'd learned a useful lesson – how to accept defeat with dignity (and how annoying a bad winner is).

Key reminders

- Create a CV for every stage of your child's journey.

- Prepare your child for daunting situations like playdates in which they are going into uncharted territory.

- You can't plan for everything, and you don't need to. If you have given your child the skills they need to cope with unexpected or difficult situations, they should be fine.

- Being prepared does not mean you're neurotic or a panicker.

- Always check in with your child before you invite a friend round. They may not have enjoyed their playdate.

- Prepare your child for how different secondary school will be to primary school.

- Prepare your child for dealing with things going wrong.

Conclusion

Although I love being a parent, I haven't always enjoyed the journey, nor been able to enjoy parenting. But I love my boys, watching them grow into amazing young men and seeing them totally comfortable with who they are. That's been amazing.

Has parenting been what I expected? Not even slightly. I have said and done things I swore I would never do when I became a parent. Would I do them again? Probably yes, but hopefully to a lesser degree.

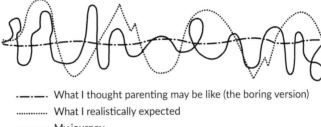

.—.—. What I thought parenting may be like (the boring version)
.... What I realistically expected
——— My journey

Reflecting on my own parenting style and skills (can we call them that?) has made me realise we are all pretty awesome parents and caregivers. Each and every one of my friends is amazing. They do things differently to myself and each other, but what they do is awesome. Once they understand their conundrum kids, they all truly accept and appreciate them. They can then guide them to connect, achieve and navigate.

That said, I wish someone had told me what parenting would really be like. I wish someone had said:

- There is no perfect parent.

- You are good enough.

- You will make mistakes.

- Trust your instincts.

- Do more of what makes you happy – and less of what makes you uncomfortable.

- Don't rush – enjoy your journey.

- Play to connect.

- Tell your partner how you're feeling.

- A happy child is better than a clean house.

- Comparison is the thief of joy (Theodore Roosevelt).

- Guilt is just a word.

- Be kind to yourself.

- Look at the dessert menu first – the best is yet to come.

My work as an OT is incredibly rewarding. Each family I work with teaches me more about life and myself. Working intensely with others makes me feel more connected and in tune with my own family.

I am grateful for being involved in guiding, supporting and facilitating greater connection and achievement with the hundreds of families I have worked with, and know that my unique insights into autism, domestic violence, ADHD, depression and anxiety have led me to this point: the point of knowing that all families and children CAN.

Connect – Achieve – Navigate.

Acknowledgements

There are so many people who have helped guide me along my journey – not just while writing this book, but throughout my life. If I forget anyone, know that it's because my ADHD meds have worn off, or I've forgotten to take it.

To everyone at Rethink Publishing – Verity for helping me with the structure, Joe for the creativity with the cover, Helen and Alison for the amazing edits, and Lucy – for all your support throughout.

To all the unbelievably amazing children and families I've met and had the privilege of working with – you inspire me. You make me want to be better and do more.

My fantastic beta-readers:

Steph Caswell – your honest feedback gave me so much clarity and direction. Thank you for inspiring me to write.

Maggie Morton – thank you for sticking with it, and not getting too distracted – your input was invaluable, and I am so glad we met all those years ago in Denver. You are awesome.

Cathy Farmer – thank you for the clever words and the lovely chats in the waiting room. You gave me the push (shove) to do it. You're an amazing cheerleader.

Claire Wood – you know me so well, and you totally get me.

My amazing team at Sensational Kids – your support and patience through some tough times has been invaluable. Thank you for putting up with my distractibility.

Giselle Monbiot – look what your support has led to! Thank you for encouraging me.

My wonderful tribe of phenomenal women:

Philippa – you are phenomenal – you unknowingly supported me with your random and discombobulated messages, and your early morning phone calls were a welcome distraction.

Anele – you are so wonderful and inspiring – dankie.

Rekha – my utterly crazy friend – you totally get me.

Suzy – I love having a friend who I can always blame for the trouble I get into – you definitely made me do it (and this).

Kirsten – you are the sweariest, most genuine, most loyal sister from another mister a girl could ask for. Thank you for being you. You rock, you little fireball.

Claire H – you feed my soul, you inspire me, you challenge me, and you listen. Thank you for letting me be a part of your journey.

Tina – the best neighbour and friend ever – thank you for making me a part of your crazy family.

Claire F – don't ever change. You are one of the most loyal, encouraging and supportive people I know. I can't wait for the day when you realise just how brilliant and amazing you are. Thank you for all the carrot cake and aerial yoga.

My parents – I love you beyond words. Thank you for everything you gave me and for always loving me. I would not be who I am today had it not been for you. My darling brother – I wish you could see me now. Thank you for all that you did for me. I love you and I didn't say it enough when you were alive. And to the best sisters Zana, Zabie and Tash – I love you for always making me look so clever and witty and funny. I couldn't wish for better sisters – you're perfectly nutty and wonderful and crazy and awesome as you are. Your courage and resilience inspire me to do better. Thank you for raising me, raising me up and always, ALWAYS believing in me.

Buster – I am so glad you can't talk otherwise you would have told everyone how I always say that you're my favourite. Thank you for being the best emotional support dog I could ever ask for. Buddy – you are totally wild, bolshy, and crazy, and perfect – but please calm down!

Tash – your strength, courage and bravery never cease to amaze me – you've kept me going and always remind me that I am loved. You are the best sister-mother-friend-fan I could ever ask for. Thanks for bringing Stephen into my life – he won't read this so I can be nice and say how much his support and encouragement means to me.

Xavier and Noah – you have brilliantly put up with my ramblings, grumpiness, shouty rants, early morning/late night spring clean sessions, embarrassing kitchen dancing, weird obsessions, inability to complete a sentence, humming, meerkat-like focus, and impulsiveness, without locking me in a room. Bravo! Thank you for letting me experiment on you and try out every new technique and assessment. You both make me so proud every single day.

And of course, leaving the best to last. Zayn.

Wow – what a ride. You are my lobster. This book would definitely not have happened without your constant love and support. Thank you for rescuing me all those years ago in the IT lab in Cape Town. You have put up with my batshit crazy weirdness for so long it is no wonder your hair is so grey! You've seen me at my best and my worst (yikes), and you never gave up on me. Love you always, your oj xx

The Author

Aniesa Blore graduated in December 1999 with a degree in occupational therapy, and immediately started her career working with children and young adults in an eating disorder unit, as well as doing some mainstream paediatric occupational therapy. She loves learning about mental health and has been amazed to see how often it is disregarded, especially when it comes to boys and young men. And this is where the seeds of *Parenting The Conundrum Child* were planted.

Aniesa moved to London at the end of 2000, where she started off as a locum working for the National Health Service. She then spent six wonderful years at The Children's Trust – a tremendous charity for children with acquired brain injuries. In 2008, she set up Sensational Kids Therapy, and now employs a team of OTs and therapy assistants to provide occupational therapy to schools in and around Greater London and Surrey.

As well as managing her team, Aniesa continues to provide direct therapy to some of the most complex children in the UK, guiding them and their families to greater connection – connection is at the root of achieving and navigating through life. She is an advanced practitioner in Ayres Sensory Integration® and has completed two levels of mentorship at the Star Institute in Denver under Dr Lucy Jane Miller. She acts as an expert witness in special educational needs and disability (SEND) tribunals and has provided lessons on occupational therapy for the National Oak Academy.

Aniesa has been married to Zayn for over twenty-one years and is mother to two young men who never cease to amaze her. She still smiles and thinks, 'I made those', but has to admit that she and Zayn now enjoy being able to go on holidays without their boys.

You can connect with Aniesa at:

- www.linkedin.com/in/aniesablore
- www.linkedin.com/company/sensationalkids
- www.facebook.com/sensationalkidslondon
- aniesablore.com
- www.sensationalkids.co.uk
- www.theconundrumchild.co.uk

Lightning Source UK Ltd.
Milton Keynes UK
UKHW021255290822
407874UK00010B/223